SPOOKY TALES
about WITCHES, Ghosts, Goblins DEMONS, and Such

SPOOKY TALES
about WITCHES, Ghosts, Goblins
DEMONS, and Such

compiled by

Mildred Corell Luckhardt

drawings by Ralph McDonald

Nashville • New York   Abingdon Press

THE COMPILER AND PUBLISHERS WISH TO THANK INDIVIDUALS AND PUB-
LISHERS FOR THEIR PERMISSION TO USE COPYRIGHTED MATERIAL AS FOLLOWS:

Abingdon Press for "Trina's Halloween Adventure" from *Trina's Boxcar* by Patricia M. Martin, copyright © 1967 by Abingdon Press.

Coward-McCann, Inc., and the *Saturday Review of Literature* for lines from "The Bad Kitten" from *Compass Rose* by Elizabeth Coatsworth. Copyright 1929 and copyright renewed (1967) by Elizabeth Coatsworth. Reprinted by permission of Coward-McCann, Inc.

Mrs. Willard G. Crichton for "The Ghost of Captain Brand," adapted from *Howard Pyle's Book of Pirates* by Howard Pyle, copyright 1921 and 1949.

Thomas Y. Crowell Company, Inc., for "Halloween with Onion John" from *Onion John* by Joseph Krumgold. Copyright © 1959 by Joseph Krumgold. Reprinted by permission of Thomas Y. Crowell Company, Inc., New York, publishers.

E. P. Dutton & Company, Inc., and the Bodley Head, for "How Finn Won His Father's Place" from *The High Deeds of Finn Mac Cool* by Rosemary Sutcliff. Copyright © 1967 by Rosemary Sutcliff. Published by E. P. Dutton & Co., Inc. Reprinted with the permission of E. P. Dutton & Company and The Bodley Head.

Robert B. Egan, estate of Joseph B. Egan, for "Drums of the Storm, "The People of the Night," and "The Wishing Stones," from *New Found Tales from Many Lands* by Joseph Burke Egan. Used by permission.

Mrs. Arthur Guiterman for "What the Gray Cat Sings" from *I Sing the Pioneer* by Arthur Guiterman. Used by permission.

Harcourt, Brace Jovanovich, Inc. for "Katcha and the Devil" by Parker Fillmore. Copyright 1919 by Parker

Fillmore; renewed 1947, by Louise Fillmore. Reprinted from *The Shepherd's Nosegay* by Parker Fillmore, edited by Katherine Love, by permission of Harcourt Brace Jovanovich, Inc.; and for "Hallowe'en" from *The Little Hill* by Harry Behn. Copyright 1949 by Harry Behn. Reprinted by permission of Harcourt Brace Jovanovich, Inc.

Harper & Row, Publishers, Inc. for "The Lutin in the Barn" from *Sashes Red and Blue* by Natalie Savage Carlson. Copyright © 1956 by Natalie Savage Carlson. Reprinted by permission of Harper & Row, Publishers.

Harper & Row, Publishers, Inc. and Longman Group Limited for "The Devil's Trick" from *Zlateh the Goat and Other Stories* by Isaac Bashevis Singer. Copyright © 1966 by Isaac Bashevis Singer. Reprinted by permission of Harper & Row, Publishers, and Longman Group Limited.

Holt, Rinehart and Winston, Inc. and Laurence Pollinger, Ltd. for lines from "Theme in Yellow" from *Chicago Poems* by Carl Sandburg. Copyright 1916 by Holt, Rinehart and Winston, Inc. Copyright 1944 by Carl Sandburg. Reprinted by permission of Holt, Rinehart and Winston, Inc. and of Laurence Pollinger, Ltd.

Houghton Mifflin Company and Victor Gollancz, Ltd. for "Witchcraft Trial of Kit Tyler" from *The Witch of Blackbird Pond* by Elizabeth George Speare, copyright © 1958 by Elizabeth George Speare. Reprinted by permission of Houghton Mifflin Company and of Victor Gollancz, Ltd.

Instructor magazine for "Buy Me!" by Frances Lowry, copyright © 1965, Instructor Publications. Used by permission of *Instructor* magazine.

J. B. Lippincott Company for "The Horned Woman" from *The Talking Tree and Other Stories* selected by Augusta Baker. Copyright © 1955 by J. B. Lippincott Company. Reprinted by permission of the publishers.

William Morrow and Company, Inc. for "The Nick of Time" from *The 13th Is Magic* by Joan Howard, copyright 1950 by Lothrop, Lee & Shepherd Company. Reprinted by permission of Lothrop, Lee & Shephard Company and the proprietors.

The Macmillan Company for lines from "Witches' Song" from the book *Summer Green* by Elizabeth Coatsworth, copyright 1948 by The Macmillan Company. Reprinted with permission.

G. P. Putnam's Sons for "Tamlane" from *More English Fairy Tales,* collected and edited by Joseph Jacobs. Reprinted by permission.

St. Martin's Press, New York, and The Macmillan Company, London, for "How a Devil Danced to Death" from *Liberian Folklore* by A. Doris Banks Henries, copyright © 1966, A. Doris Banks Henries. Reprinted by permission of the publishers.

The Society of Authors for a portion of "The Ride-by-Nights" by Walter de la Mare. Permission to reprint granted by The Literary Trustees of Walter de la Mare and The Society of Authors as their representative.

The University of North Carolina Press for one legend from *The Devil's Tramping Ground and Other North Carolina Stories* by John Hardin, copyright 1949, The University of North Carolina Press; and for "Ghostly Gold" from *Tar Heel Ghosts* by John Hardin, copyright 1954, The University of North Carolina Press. Reprinted by permission of the publishers.

Miss Eleanor W. Vinton for "Parson Walker Preaches on Witchcraft." Reprinted by permission of the author.

To
George William
and his sisters and cousins
and to
the many friendly girls and boys and grown-ups
who read my books and often write me about them;
and to all those in many places with whom I talk
about books and read stories from my books—
GOOD WISHES TO EACH OF YOU AND MAY
YOU ALL ENJOY *SPOOKY TALES*.

Thank You--

People from many different places have helped in preparing this book. The list would be far too long if I mentioned all the friendly educators, librarians, other friends, and members of my family to whom I have turned for help and encouragement in my work, but I do thank each one most gratefully.

All the librarians in Rye Library, Rye, New York have helped me in my spooky search, especially Miss Doris Bird, Mrs. Howard Sweeney, Mrs. Robert Lagey, Miss Mary Lyon, and Miss Ruth Harry, director of the library. Mrs. Elizabeth Boyle of Rye's Midland School was helpful, and Rabbi Robert Rothman, also of Rye, guided me toward legends of the Golem and furnished much related information. Among others from Rye are Miss Vera Kelly, who has given me ideas and checked the manuscript; Mrs. Elizabeth Pollard, who has worked hard helping me sweep the witches out of covens onto the typewriter and into this book; Miss Joanne Jacobs of Rye; and Mrs. Miles Chelimer of Larchmont.

From the City of New York help came from Mrs. Eloise Shelton, librarian at Joseph Burger Junior High School. Mr. William Lindeman, New York attorney with international connections, searched for information about "wicca" and other ancient rites and their present-day revival. Dr. Thomas B. Davis, professor of history, Hunter College of the City University of New York, shared with me some of his store of knowledge and made valuable suggestions about part of my manuscript.

Mrs. James Sherron of Hilltown, New Jersey, furnished documented information about a New Jersey witch-burning of the early 1700s.

Resource material on ghost stories was sent me by the Morganton, North Carolina, Library and by Mrs. William Herbert Kibler of Morgantown. From Pascagoula, Mississippi, Mr. Robert Egan has given me generous assistance and encouragement in the compilation of this and previous books.

Teachers in the public schools of Boothbay Harbor, Maine, who have sent me material are Miss Marjorie McGlauflin and Miss Mary Campbell. Librarians at the University of Maine—Portland also have been helpful, and so have Mrs. Clifford McGlauflin of Portland and Mrs. Kenneth Larrabee, librarian of Merrill Memorial Library of Yarmouth, Maine.

Legends of the Southwest have been sent to me by Mrs. Ernestine McSweeney of Saguaro Branch of the Phoenix Public Library System.

School students from Connecticut to Arizona have searched for suitable material, helped me check over the manuscript, made suggestions about the articles, and discussed with me (and with their friends to whom they read the manuscript) such characters as "that guy Samhain" and "Jack-O-Lantern who was such a mean guy even the devil didn't want him." Among those students are Amy, Corell, and Lucy Anne Luckhardt of Kiva School, Scottsdale, Arizona; Marianne Kenney of Helen Keller Middle School, Easton, Connecticut; and Allison Barclay of Moorestown Friends Junior High School, Moorestown, New Jersey.

From Toronto, Canada, Miss Doris Scott, librarian of Boys and Girls House, has responded promptly whenever I have asked her for needed information in connection with this and several previous books.

To each person mentioned I say "Thank you" once again. It would be difficult to name everyone who has worked hard to bring this book to completion. I am grateful to all those who have spent their time, skill, and artistry. Among them is artist Ralph McDonald whose illustrations add a really spooky touch.

And now I wish to say to Anne Izard, director of children's services, Westchester County Library System, "A very special *thank you* for your encouragement in my writing efforts, your suggestions of resource material, and for allowing me to share in the magic you bring to book discussions."

—MILDRED CORELL LUCKHARDT

Rye, New York
Halloween, 1970

Contents

13

SPOOKY TALES
about WITCHES, Ghosts, Goblins
DEMONS, and Such

The Bell-man

From noise of Scare-fires rest ye free,
From Murders—*Benedicite*.
From all mischances, that may fright
Your pleasing slumbers in the night:
Mercie secure ye all, and keep
The Goblin from ye, while ye sleep.
Past one aclock, and almost two,
My Masters all, *Good day to you!*

—ROBERT HERRICK

Goblins, Devils, Demons, and Such

From very ancient times many people have been afraid of the unknown, the spooky, the mysterious. Knowing little about science, they have imagined that all sorts of strange creatures and evil spirits are everywhere, ready to harm them. These creatures are not mortals but enemies of mortals. Evil spirits might have different names in different parts of the world, but everywhere people have thought they had to appease them or else outwit them. Stories of how humans outwit demons and the like have long entertained people in many lands.

Sometimes, even farm animals are said to outwit these scary, unearthly creatures, as in the story of the Billy Goats Gruff and the horrible *troll* that lived under the bridge. *Trolls,* strange beings from Scandinavia, are different sizes, from giant to dwarf. They dread noise and sometimes can be driven away if church bells are rung loud and long. Hating the sun, they live in dark forests or underground or under bridges.

Since many people have always feared the dark, they have imagined that all the evil beings—wicked creatures of darkness—are most dangerous at night. *Goblins* usually work their mischief in the dark. They are known by different names, including kobold or lutin, and they are always causing trouble for people. They often haunt groves and caves, one famous cave being The Goblins' Cave by Loch Katrine in Scotland. Some goblins are monstrous. Some are tiny and carry will-o'-the-wisp lights that lure travelers at night through bogs and swamps and often make them hopelessly lost. Sometimes goblins, lutins, and such creatures ride horses at night and tangle their manes and tails.

Hobgoblins are thought to stay close to the house, especially near the fireplace where food is kept warm on a flat projection, or hob. Hobgoblins sometimes are called "hobs" for short, and they stir up trouble when angry. So the expression, to "raise hob," has come to mean to raise a storm of mischief as the hobs did.

Monsters may be hideously large, unnatural, evil beings or weird, cruel animals. In a legend more than a thousand years old a fierce monster named Grendel used to devour a number of leaders of the Danes each night. A brave hero named Beowulf crossed the sea and slew the wicked monster. Later Beowulf was drawn into a fierce battle with Grendel's mother, an evil, frightful water-hag. Eventually he overcame the forces of evil that threatened to destroy the people, and once more the land was secure. The "Beowulf" legend is the oldest preserved Anglo-Saxon epic poem and has come down from the eighth century.

The *Goblin Spider* of Japan, by its magic, grows to great size at night, weaves a tremendous web, and lures people to their doom in it. In tales from many lands a fantastic spider causes evil and destruction, like a goblin. *Anansi,* the giant spider of West Africa, makes trouble for people through its magic. Sometimes this imaginary spider even can appear as a man.

Early tales in many lands speak of the supernatural power of *Snakes,* almost always evil and very clever. Some snakes have more than one head. At times, though, snakes have been said to possess healing power. As a symbol of healing medicine, the caduceus is used by doctors and the Medical Corps. The caduceus is a magic wand, twined with snakes and topped by wings. It is said to have been given by the Greek god Apollo to Mercury, the messenger of the gods. Mercury used it as his symbol, and it was believed to bring wealth and happiness and to have power over sleeping and waking. In general, though, snakes frighten many people and often have been used by magicians.

Besides the many animals believed to have magic powers and the scary creatures that people's imaginations conjure up, *evil spirits* have always been thought to exist everywhere in nature. They lurke in pools or streams, or the sea, ready to pull people under. They hide in the fields and trees, ready to pounce. Some people say a person should be careful not to anger these spirits, or else he must try to outwit them. Sometimes it has been imagined that spirit drums could be heard in a storm and that they have lured people into the spirits' power.

Sometimes these evil spirits are called *devils* or *demons* and are thought to be ruled by the Prince of Evil, the *Devil.* For centuries stories have been told about the magic power of the Devil or of minor devils. Often witches and other creatures of darkness work with the devil to enslave the soul of a person.

Many stories tell of a person who, wanting more power or riches, was persuaded to "sell his soul" to the devil so he would get what he wanted. The deal seemed harmless at first. Usually the devil came as a good-looking person who talked in such a friendly way that his victim did not recognize him as the evil power or see the danger in making a pact with him. Because the man wanted so much to get what he wished for, he found it easy to do for the devil what he once thought was wrong. He believed that after he had gained the prize he would return to being honest and good. At the end of some of these tales, the devil showed no mercy, and the man's life and happiness were destroyed. In others some brave and good person or perhaps an angel was able to save the man from the devil, and the man once more tried to live a good life.

Among the many names for the devil are Satan, Beelzebub, Diabolo, Mephisto, Mephistopheles. In the story about Dr. Faustus, or Faust, the devil is called Mephistopheles. This story was told in German about two hundred years ago by Johann Wolfgang von Goethe. Dr. Faust was a great scholar, a good man with high ideals; but he was unhappy. He longed for almost divine knowledge and wanted to shake off whatever kept him bound to this world.

Then along came the devil and very smoothly persuaded Faust to stop trying to reach his high ideals and to let himself go in a life of complete, selfish pleasure. Mephistopheles ordered a witch to make a pleasing drug that would change Faust into a reckless, pleasure-mad young man who took whatever he wanted and could not be faithful to anyone he thought he loved.

Faust lost all sense of right and wrong and did whatever he chose for the sake of excitement and pleasure. After many weeks of such folly, the devil took Faust to the Witches' Fete on a barren mountain on May Day Eve. A goblin named Wisp led the way with his goblin light. Mephistopheles took Faust from one wild experience to another, chasing madly after new excitements, new pleasures.

Urged on by the devil, they kept on the go from country to country, chasing after whatever was sensational or extravagant. At last, Faust was disgusted and sick of that sort of life. He was very sad as he thought of the wicked things he had done, the time he had wasted, and the people he had hurt while he was in the devil's power. Little by little, his old dreams of goodness and kindness returned. He decided that he would do everything he could for the good of other people. Once more hope and happiness came to him, and the power of his good thoughts and plans helped him to have courage to fight against the devil's evil power.

Suddenly in the midst of this fight, Faust died. The devil shrieked, "His soul is mine!" and called hosts of devils to carry Faust's soul to Hell. But the good Powers of Light rescued his soul from the evil Powers of Darkness, and an angel choir sang for joy as Faust was carried to safety and happiness.

Some other well-known stories about the devil are "The Devil and Tom Walker" by Washington Irving, and "The Devil and Daniel Webster" by Stephen Vincent Benet. All through history there are accounts of persons who are tempted to worship the Devil or Satan.

Besides the many serious stories about the devil's getting power over a person, there are many very funny stories in which the devil is outwitted. Czechoslovakia is one of the countries that enjoys such folktales. In many lands people tell stories of the way a devil plays the violin so gaily that those who hear it begin to dance and have to keep dancing and dancing until they drop. But sometimes a very smart person finds a way to outsmart a devil, even in dancing.

In many places, frightening tales are told of the way demons and the nature gods work together to punish people. Often these creatures, with their weird helpers, meet on a mountain before descending on the people. For instance, some Indian tales say that the Thunder Gods live on Superstition Mountain in Arizona. Others say that the Devil lurks there ready to kill anyone who dares come to steal his gold from the mine. Since so many people have been greedy for that gold, some Indian tales claim that the Thunder Gods of Greed meet there every third moon in council with other eerie supernatural beings.

Greedy persons, according to stories told throughout the world, usually are easier prey for goblins, demons, and other evil spirits than are honest, generous persons. Also, the evil creatures hate the light of truth or the light of day. As in the story of Faust, many frightening creatures are in league with the devil to harm man, and their wicked work is done most frequently at night. With the first light of dawn or the first rooster's crow, they disappear into the air or flee back to their dark, dank shelters.

—MILDRED CORELL LUCKHARDT

The Gobble-uns 'll Git You
Ef You Don't Watch Out!

Little Orphant Annie says, when the blaze is blue,
An' the lamp-wick sputters, an' the wind goes *woo-oo!*
An' you hear the crickets quit, an' the moon is gray,
An' the lightnin'-bugs in dew is all squenched away,—
You better mind yer parunts, an' yer teachurs fond an' dear,
An' churish them 'at loves you, an' dry the orphant's tear,
An' he'p the pore an' needy ones 'at clusters all about,
Er the Gobble-uns 'll git you
         Ef you
            Don't
               Watch
                   Out!

—JAMES WHITCOMB RILEY

Katcha and the Devil
The Story of a Clinging Vine
A Czechoslovak Fairy Tale

There was once a woman named Katcha who lived in a village where she owned her own cottage and garden. She had money besides but little good it did her because she was such an ill-tempered vixen that nobody, not even the poorest laborer, would marry her. Nobody would even work for her, no matter what she paid, for she couldn't open her mouth without scolding, and whenever she scolded she raised her shrill voice until you could hear it a mile away. The older she grew the worse she became until by the time she was forty she was as sour as vinegar.

Now as it always happens in a village, every Sunday afternoon there was a dance either at the burgomaster's, or at the tavern. As soon as the bagpipes sounded, the boys all crowded into the room and the girls gathered outside and looked in the windows. Katcha was always the first at the window. The music would strike up and the boys would beckon the girls to come in and dance, but no one ever beckoned Katcha. Even when she paid the piper no one ever asked her to dance. Yet she came Sunday after Sunday just the same.

One Sunday afternoon as she was hurrying to the tavern she thought to herself: "Here I am getting old and yet I've never once danced with a boy! Plague take it, today I'd dance with the devil if he asked me!"

She was in a fine rage by the time she reached the tavern, where she sat down near the stove and looked around to see what girls the boys had invited to dance.

Suddenly a stranger in hunter's green came in. He sat down at a table near Katcha and ordered drink. When the serving maid brought it, he reached over to Katcha and asked her to drink with him. At first she was much taken back at this attention, then she pursed her lips coyly and pretended to refuse, but finally she accepted.

When they had finished drinking, he pulled a ducat from his pocket, tossed it to the piper, and called out:

"Clear the floor, boys! This is for Katcha and me alone!"

The boys snickered and the girls giggled hiding behind each other and stuffing their aprons into their mouths so that Katcha wouldn't hear them laughing. But Katcha wasn't noticing them at all. Katcha was dancing with a fine young man! If the whole world had been laughing at her, Katcha wouldn't have cared.

The stranger danced with Katcha all afternoon and all evening. Not once did he dance with any one else. He brought her marzipan and sweet drinks and, when the hour came to go home, he escorted her through the village.

"Ah," sighed Katcha when they reached her cottage and it was time to part, "I wish I could dance with you forever!"

"Very well," said the stranger. "Come with me."

"Where do you live?"

"Put your arm around my neck and I'll tell you."

Katcha put both arms about his neck and instantly the man changed into a devil and flew straight down to hell.

At the gates of hell he stopped and knocked.

His comrades came and opened the gates and when they saw that he was exhausted, they tried to take Katcha off his neck. But Katcha held on tight and nothing they could do or say would make her budge.

The devil finally had to appear before the Prince of Darkness himself with Katcha still glued to his neck.

"What's that thing you've got around your neck?" the Prince asked.

So the devil told how as he was walking about on earth he had heard Katcha say she would dance with the devil himself if he asked her. "So I asked her to dance with me," the devil said. "Afterwards just to frighten her a little I brought her down to hell. And now she won't let go of me!"

"Serve you right, you dunce!" the Prince said. "How often have I told you to use common sense when you go wandering around on earth! You might have known Katcha would never let go of a man once she had him!"

"I beg your Majesty to make her let go!" the poor devil implored.

"I will not!" said the Prince. "You'll have to carry her back to earth yourself and get rid of her as best you can. Perhaps this will be a lesson to you."

So the devil, very tired and very cross, shambled back to earth with Katcha still clinging to his neck. He tried every way to get her off. He promised her wooded hills and rich meadows if she let him go. He cajoled her, he cursed her, but all to no avail. Katcha still held on.

Breathless and discouraged he came at last to a meadow where a shepherd, wrapped in a great shaggy sheepskin coat, was tending his flocks. The devil transformed himself into an ordinary looking man so that the shepherd didn't recognize him.

"Hi, there," the shepherd said, "what's that you're carrying?"

"Don't ask me," the devil said with a sigh. "I'm so worn out I'm nearly dead. I was walking yonder not thinking of anything at all when along comes a woman and jumps on my back and won't let go. I'm trying to carry her to the nearest village to get rid of her there, but I don't believe I'm able. My legs are giving out."

The shepherd, who was a good-natured chap, said: "I tell you what: I'll help you. I can't leave my sheep long, but I'll carry her halfway."

"Oh," said the devil, "I'd be very grateful if you did!"

So the shepherd yelled at Katcha: "Hi, there, you! Catch hold of me!"

When Katcha saw that the shepherd was a handsome youth, she let go of the devil and leapt upon the shepherd's back, catching hold of the collar of his sheepskin coat.

Now the young shepherd soon found that the long shaggy coat and Katcha made a pretty heavy load for walking. In a few moments he was sick of his bargain and began casting about for some way of getting rid of Katcha.

Presently he came to a pond and he thought to himself that he'd like to throw her in. He wondered how he could do it. Perhaps he could manage it by throwing in his greatcoat with her. The coat was so loose that he thought he could slip out of it without Katcha's discovering what he was doing. Very cautiously he slipped out one arm. Katcha didn't move. He slipped out the other arm. Still Katcha didn't move. He unlooped the first button. Katcha noticed nothing. He unlooped the second button. Still Katcha noticed nothing. He unlooped the third button and kerplunk! he had pitched coat and Katcha and all into the middle of the pond!

When he got back to his sheep, the devil looked at him in amazement.

"Where's Katcha?" he gasped.

"Oh," the shepherd said, pointing over his shoulder with his thumb, "I decided to leave her up yonder in a pond."

"My dear friend," the devil cried, "I thank you! You have done me a great favor. If it hadn't been for you I might be carrying Katcha till doomsday. I'll never forget you and some time I'll reward you. As you don't know who it is you've helped, I must tell you I'm a devil."

With these words the devil vanished.

For a moment the shepherd was dazed. Then he laughed and said to himself: "Well, if they're all as stupid as he is, we ought to be a match for them!"

The country where the shepherd lived was ruled over by a dissolute young duke who passed his days in riotous living and his nights in carousing. He gave over the affairs of state to two governors who were as bad as he. With extortionate taxes and unjust fines they robbed the people until the whole land was crying out against them.

Now one day for amusement the duke summoned an astrologer to court and ordered him to read in the planets the fate of himself and his two governors. When the astrologer had cast a horoscope for each of the three reprobates, he was greatly disturbed and tried to dissuade the duke from questioning him further.

"Such danger," he said, "threatens your life and the lives of your two governors that I fear to speak."

"Whatever it is," said the duke, "speak. But I warn you to speak the truth, for if what you say does not come to pass you will forfeit your life."

The astrologer bowed and said: "Hear then, oh Duke, what the planets foretell: Before the second quarter of the moon, on such and such a day, at such and such an hour, a devil will come and carry off the two governors. At the full of the moon on such and such a day, at such and such an hour, the same devil will come for your Highness and carry you off to hell."

The duke pretended to be unconcerned but in his heart he was deeply shaken. The voice of the astrologer sounded to him like the voice of judgment and for the first time conscience began to trouble him.

As for the governors, they couldn't eat a bite of food and were carried from the palace half dead with fright. They piled their ill-gotten wealth into wagons and rode away to their castles, where they barred all the doors and windows in order to keep the devil out.

The duke reformed. He gave up his evil ways and corrected the abuses of state in the hope of averting if possible his cruel fate.

The poor shepherd had no inkling of any of these things. He tended his flocks from day to day and never bothered his head about the happenings in the great world.

Suddenly one day the devil appeared before him and said, "I have come, my friend, to repay you for your kindness. When the moon is in its first quarter, I was to carry off the former governors of this land because they robbed the poor and gave the duke evil counsel. However, they're behaving themselves now so they're to be given another chance. But they don't know this. Now on such and such a day do you go to the first castle where a crowd of people will be assembled. When a cry goes up and the gates open and I come dragging out the governor, do you step up to me and say: 'What do you mean by this? Get out of here or there'll be trouble!' I'll pretend to be greatly frightened and make off. Then ask the governor to pay you two bags of gold, and if he haggles just threaten to call me back. After that go on to the castle of the second governor and do the same thing and demand the same pay. I warn you, though, be prudent with the money and use it only for good. When the moon is full, I'm to carry off the duke himself, for he was so wicked that he's to have no second chance. So don't try to save him, for if you do you'll pay for it with your own skin. Don't forget!"

The shepherd remembered carefully everything the devil told him. When the moon was in its first quarter he went to the first castle. A great crowd of people was gathered outside waiting to see the devil carry away the governor.

Suddenly there was a loud cry of despair, the gates of the castle opened, and there was the devil dragging out the governor. He, poor man, was half dead with fright.

The shepherd elbowed his way through the crowd, took the governor by the hand, and pushed the devil roughly aside.

"What do you mean by this?" he shouted. "Get out of here or there'll be trouble!"

Instantly the devil fled and the governor fell on his knees before the shepherd and kissed his hands and begged him to state what he wanted in reward. When the shepherd asked for two bags of gold, the governor ordered that they be given him without delay.

Then the shepherd went to the castle of the second governor and went through exactly the same performance.

It goes without saying that the duke soon heard of the shepherd, for he had been anxiously awaiting the fate of the two governors. At once he sent a wagon with four horses to fetch the shephard to the palace and when the shepherd arrived he begged him piteously to rescue him likewise from the devil's clutches.

"Master," the shepherd answered, "I cannot promise you anything. I have to consider my own safety. You have been a great sinner, but if you really want to reform, if you really want to rule your people justly and kindly and wisely as becomes a true ruler, then indeed I will help you even if I have to suffer hellfire in your place."

The duke declared that with God's help he would mend his ways and the shepherd promised to come back on the fatal day.

With grief and dread the whole country awaited the coming of the full moon. In the first place the people had greeted the astrologer's prophecy with joy, but since the duke had reformed their feelings for him had changed.

Time sped fast as time does whether joy be coming or sorrow and all too soon the fatal day arrived.

Dressed in black and pale with fright, the duke sat expecting the arrival of the devil.

Suddenly the door flew open and the devil stood before him. He paused a moment and then he said, politely:

"Your time has come, Lord Duke, and I am here to get you!"

Without a word the duke arose and followed the devil to the courtyard, which was filled with a great multitude of people.

At that moment the shepherd, all out of breath, came pushing his way through the crowd, and ran straight at the devil, shouting out:

"What do you mean by this? Get out of here or there'll be trouble!"

"What do *you* mean?" whispered the devil. "Don't you remember what I told you?"

"Hush!" the shepherd whispered back. "I don't care anything about the duke. This is to warn you! You know Katcha? She's alive and she's looking for you!"

The instant the devil heard the name of Katcha he turned and fled.

All the people cheered the shepherd, while the shepherd himself laughed in his sleeve to think that he had taken in the devil so easily.

As for the duke, he was so grateful to the shepherd that he made him his chief counselor and loved him as a brother. And well he might, for the shepherd was a sensible man and always gave him sound advice.

—RETOLD BY PARKER FILLMORE

The Devil's Trick
A Yiddish Folktale

The snow had been falling for three days and three nights. Houses were snowed in and windowpanes covered with frost flowers. The wind whistled in the chimneys. Gusts of snow somersaulted in the cold air.

The devil's wife rode on her hoop, with a broom in one hand and a rope in the other. Before her ran a white goat with a black beard and twisted horns. Behind her strode the devil with his cobweb face, holes instead of eyes, hair to his shoulders, and legs as long as stilts.

In a one-room hut, with a low ceiling and soot-covered walls, sat David, a poor boy with a pale face and black eyes. He was alone with his baby brother on the first night of Hanukkah. His father had gone to the village to buy corn, but three days had passed and he had not returned home. David's mother had gone to look for her husband, and she too had not come back. The baby slept in his cradle. In the Hanukkah lamp flickered the first candle.

David was so worried he could not stay home any longer. He put on his padded coat and his cap with earlaps, made sure that the baby was covered, and went out to look for his parents.

That was what the devil had been waiting for. He immediately whipped up the storm. Black clouds covered the sky. David could hardly see in the thick darkness. The frost burned his face. The snow fell dry and heavy as salt. The wind caught David by his coattails and tried to lift him up off the ground. He was surrounded by laughter, as if from a thousand imps.

David realized the goblins were after him. He tried to turn back and go home, but he could not find his way. The snow and darkness swallowed *everything*. It became clear to him that the devils must have caught his parents. Would they get him also? But heaven and earth have vowed that the devil may never succeed completely in his tricks. No matter how shrewd the devil is, he will always make a mistake, especially on Hanukkah.

The powers of evil had managed to hide the stars, but they could not extinguish the single Hanukkah candle. David saw its light and ran toward it. The devil ran after him. The devil's wife followed on her hoop, yelling and waving her broom, trying to lasso him with her rope. David ran even more quickly than they, and reached the hut just ahead of the devil. As David opened the door the devil tried to get in with him. David managed to slam the door behind him. In the rush the devil's tail got stuck in the door.

"Give me back my tail," the devil screamed.

And David replied, "Give me back my father and mother."

The devil swore that he knew nothing about them, but David did not let himself be fooled.

"You kidnapped them, cursed Devil," David said. He picked up a sharp ax and told the devil that he would cut off his tail.

"Have pity on me. I have only one tail," the devil cried. And to his wife he said, "Go quickly to the cave behind the black mountains and bring back the man and woman we led astray."

His wife sped away on her hoop and soon brought the couple back. David's father sat on the hoop holding on to the witch by her hair; his mother came riding on the white goat, its black beard clasped tightly in her hands.

"Your mother and father are here. Give me my tail," said the devil.

David looked through the keyhole and saw his parents were really there. He wanted to open the door at once and let them in, but he was not ready to free the devil.

He rushed over to the window, took the Hanukkah candle, and singed the devil's tail. "Now, Devil, you will always remember," he cried, "Hanukkah is no time for making trouble."

Then at last he opened the door. The devil licked his singed tail and ran off with his wife to the land where no people walk, no cattle tread, where the sky is copper and the earth is iron.

—RETOLD BY ISAAC BASHEVIS SINGER

The Lutin in the Barn
A French Canadian Tale

It is a long time since the lutin has been seen in Canada. That is not because the horses have turned into automobiles. French Canada is still a place for horses on farms and on the roads. It must be Tonton LeBlanc who drove the lutin away forever.

Tonton had the fastest horse in the Beauce. His Rosa-mai won all the races in that part of the country. Once a week there would be a big race with every farmer for miles around riding his best horse. The prize was always a bag of potatoes or a sack of flour.

It was too bad that Tonton had no family. He could have fed a wife and twenty children with all the potatoes and flour that his fast horse Rosa-mai won in the races.

Tonton didn't think that he needed a wife or children as long as he had Rosa-mai. He moved to a little room over the stable so he could be close to his horse and watch her at all times. He had a great fear that some night a thief would break into his barn and steal Rosa-mai.

One morning Tonton LeBlanc went down to feed his horse her oats.

To his great surprise, Rosa-mai was wearily leaning her head against the manger as if her legs couldn't hold her up. Her black coat was covered with white sweat. Her long mane was tangled in untidy loops.

Tonton was horrified. He wiped her off carefully with his own towel. He combed her mane carefully with his own comb.

"Some rascal has been riding you," he said to Rosa-mai. "Who was he?"

Of course he received no answer, and he didn't really expect one.

Tonton LeBlanc lifted her hoofs, one after another. Aha! He was right. A shoe was gone from her left hind foot.

Tonton let her rest and eat her oats. Then he put the bridle on her head and the saddle on her back. He rode to the blacksmith's shop in the village.

He found the blacksmith busy at his forge. He was surrounded by the usual men who had nothing to do but stand around in the blacksmith shop and chew pigtail tobacco.

Tonton told the blacksmith about the sad way in which he had found his horse that morning.

The men with nothing to do crowded around him. They looked at Rosa-mai's hoof with the shoe missing. They looked at her damp black coat. They looked at her thick mane and my faith, the untidy loops were still there, although Tonton had combed them out so carefully.

"The lutin is riding her," said one of the men.

"The loops will not comb out of her mane until it rains again," said another.

"Tatata!" exclaimed Tonton. "A likely cock-and-donkey story! Some young rascal in the countryside is riding her. I will catch him tonight."

That night Tonton LeBlanc laid a trap for the rascal who was riding his horse. He got a ball of string. He tied one end of it to the handle of the barn door. He unwound the ball through the stable, up the ladder, under his door, over the floor to his bed. When he went to bed, he put his gun on the floor beside him. Then he tied the other end of the string to his big toe.

"When the rascal pulls the stable door open," he told his gun, "it will jerk my toe. Then it will be your turn to do something."

Tonton LeBlanc closed his eyes and fell fast asleep. He slept as soundly as an old shoe. When he opened his eyes again, it was morning. His toe was still there and his gun was still there. He knew that Rosa-mai was still there. He could hear her snuffling.

He untied the string from his toe, dressed himself, and climbed down the ladder.

There was Rosa-mai with her head leaning against the manger again. Her black coat was covered with white sweat and there were more loops in her mane. The string across the stable had been cut in two. How had the rascal managed to do that?

Tonton was mad like two wolves.

He vowed that he would not sleep a wink the next night. And he kept that vow. "Parbleau," how he kept that vow!

He blew out his lantern so the rascal riding Rosa-mai would think he was asleep. He laid flat on the floor with his ear to a crack.

As his big clock struck twelve, there was a great "berdi-berda" in the stable below. He heard Rosa-mai whinny and kick at the door. Then, "helas!" He couldn't find a match to the light the lantern right away.

His angry, trembling hand was just making a light when he heard Rosa-mai back out of the stable.

Tonton LeBlanc only had time to run to the window with the lantern. He opened it and leaned out. Rosa-mai came galloping below him. Tonton turned the lantern on her. A-tou-tou-tou! On her back was a monster covered with long hair. He had the face of an ape and the horns of a cow.

It was the lutin.

He rode without a saddle. His great claws were twisted in Rosa-mai's mane to keep him from falling off.

As the horse raced below Tonton's window, the lutin let go with one paw and waved to the man at the window.

"Since you are awake," he called, "I'll be back in an hour for a game of cards."

Tonton LeBlanc was terrified. He wished he had never seen the rascal. He bolted the door. Against it he pushed all the bags of potatoes and sacks of flour he had won in the races.

It seemed that he waited hours and hours in the fort of flour and potatoes.

Suddenly he heard Rosa-mai's flying hoofs. He heard the barn door groan open. He heard the ladder creak and creak.

There was a "toc, toc" on the door.

"Go away," cried Tonton.

"If I go away, I'll take your horse with me," threatened the lutin. "I will never bring her back."

Tonton LeBlanc was not a very brave man, but he loved his beautiful black horse dearly. My faith, hadn't he given up a big, warm house to live in a loft over her stable? He did not want the lutin to ride her away forever.

He took his heart in his two hands, as we say of brave people. He moved the bags of potatoes and the sacks of flour from the door.

He opened it and in walked the ugly lutin as if he were an invited guest. He looked all around Tonton's little room.

"Humph!" he snorted. "I've seen better stables than this." He walked over to the table and sat down on the stool. "Where are the cards?"

Tonton took a worn pack of cards from his drawer. He pulled up a bag of potatoes and sat down on it.

"Shall we play 'seven up'?" he asked.

The "lutin" shook his horns. "A game for cowherds," he snapped. "We will play 'slap Jacques.' I'll deal because I don't trust you."

The lutin riffled the cards between his long claws. He dealt one card to himself, one to Tonton, one to himself, one to Tonton. When he had finished dealing, he picked up his hand with his long claws. He threw a card on the table. Tonton dropped another on top of it.

The lutin leaned over the table and peeped into Tonton's hand. "Why don't you play your Jacques?" he asked.

"You are cheating," said Tonton. But he took the card back and laid the jack of spades on the table. "Slap Jacques," he said. tapping the cards lightly.

The lutin brought his huge claws down on Tonton's knuckles. "SLAP JACQUES," he bawled. "My trick."

"You have the manners of the stable, monsieur," said Tonton, rubbing his hand.

"And you have poor manners for a host," retorted the lutin. "Don't you offer food to your company?"

Tonton laid his hand down and rose from the sack of potatoes.

"I have some cold potato pie left from supper," he said. "I eat it three times a day to try to get rid of all the flour and potatoes I win in races."

Tonton went into the nook which served as his kitchen. He began cutting the cold, soggy potato pie. As he did so, he raised his eyes to the tin mirror hanging over the shelf. He looked at his scared, tired face.

Then an idea jumped from the mirror into Tonton's head. His face didn't look so tired and scared any more.

He cut two pieces of pie and then he cut a third piece of pie. He put each piece on a cracked plate. He carried them out to the table on which laid the cards.

The lutin looked at the three pieces of pie. "Why do you bring me two pieces?" he asked. "From the messy look of it, I will be doing good to force one down my gullet."

Tonton hummed a little tune. "I cut three pieces of pie because I am expecting a friend to join us shortly," he replied.

The lutin was interested. "Does he have a horse?" he asked.

"I don't know," said Tonton, "but he is one of the best horse-men in Canada."

The lutin was more interested than ever. "Do I know him?" he asked.

"You should," answered Tonton. "He is a well-known fellow. Only a few days ago all the men in the blacksmith shop were talking about him."

"What is his name?" asked the lutin.

"I only know his nickname," said Tonton. "I don't believe he has any other name." He seemed to get a sudden idea. "Come to think of it. I have a picture of him hanging in my kitchen," he said. "I will show it to you."

Tonton LeBlanc went to the nook and took the mirror down from the wall. He carried it to the lutin. He put it in his long claws.

"Does the face look familiar?" asked Tonton.

The lutin looked into the mirror. He saw the ape-like face and the long horns growing out of the head. He threw the mirror on the table in fright. He jumped up from the stool.

"Tondu" he cried. "Your friend is an ugly monster. I am not staying around here to meet *him*."

And the lutin was so frightened by the hideous face he had seen that he didn't even take time to go out the door and down the ladder. He jumped right through the window, glass and all.

Tonton LeBlanc carried the mirror down to the stable and hung it over his horse's manger—just in case the lutin should come back.

But the lutin never came back to Tonton's stable, and the next time it rained all the loops combed out of Rosa-mai's mane. The wonder of it was that the lutin never came back to the Beauce any more. Perhaps that was the last time he was ever seen in Canada. He wasn't taking any chances of meeting that ugly monster face to face.

—NATALIE SAVAGE CARLSON

The Double-Headed Snake of Newbury

Far away in the twilight time
Of every people, in every clime,
Dragons and griffins and monsters dire,
Born of water, and air, and fire,
Or nursed, like the Python, in the mud
And ooze of the old Deucalion flood,
Crawl and wriggle and foam with rage,
Through dusk tradition and ballad age.
So from the childhood of Newbury town
And its time of fable the tale comes down
Of a terror which haunted bush and brake,
The Amphisbaena, the Double Snake!

. . . .

Whether he lurked in the Oldtown fen
Or the gray earth-flax of the Devil's Den,
Or swam in the wooded Artichoke,
Or coiled by the Northman's Written Rock,
Nothing on record is left to show;
Only the fact that he lived, we know,
And left the cast of a double head
In the scaly mask which he yearly shed.
For he carried a head where his tail should be,

And the two, of course, could never agree,
But wriggled about with main and might,
Now to the left and now to the right;
Pulling and twisting this way and that
Neither knew what the other was at.
A snake with two heads, lurking so near!
Judge of the wonder, guess at the fear!
Think what ancient gossips might say,
Shaking their heads in their dreary way,
Between the meetings on Sabbath-day!
How urchins, searching at day's decline
The Common Pasture for sheep or kine,
The terrible double-ganger heard
In leafy rustle or whir of bird!

. . . .

Stories, like dragons, are hard to kill.
If the snake does not, the tale runs still
In Byfield Meadows, on Pipestave Hill.

—JOHN GREENLEAF WHITTIER

Drums of the Storm
(An American Indian Tale)

At the bottom of Lake Superior lived the evil one, Matchi Manitou. He it was who reached out long, green arms of water, curling them over the frail canoes to drag unfortunate Indians down to his deep den. He it was who spread the wicked quicksands under the feet of man and beast to suck his helpless prey down to a slow and cruel death.

When the wind shrieked and the waves roared on the shingle, the Indians crept closer to their fires and whispered in low tones, "Hear the drums! Hear Matchi Manitou beating on the drums!"

Now it happened that an Indian lived on a low bluff close to the shore. He was not a good Indian at all and on that account lived apart from the tepees of the tribe. The drums of the waves were always in his ears and he came to listen to them more and more, especially through the long hours of the night, until finally he began to understand what they said to him.

One night, when there was a great storm, and the wild wings

of the wind flapped on the sides of the tent and went roaring over
the water, the wicked Indian sat up suddenly on his sleeping-fur
and cried out to his squaw:

"The drums! Hear the drums! Listen! They are talking to me.
They say, 'Matchi Manitou waits at the water edge. Come! Come!
Come! Come! Come! Come! Come! Come!'"

"I hear nothing but the thunder of the surf," mumbled his
wife sleepily.

"You are deaf then," answered the Indian, "for the drums call
plainly, 'Come! Come! Come! Come!'"

With that the Indian sprang up, seized his medicine stick and
rushed out of the tent and down to the lake shore. His wife followed
at a distance. She saw him beat upon the water with the stick.

Slap! Slap! Slap! Slap! went the stick in perfect beat with
the waves that thundered on the beach.

Then a strange thing happened. Where the long medicine
stick beat, a dark swirling hole appeared, around which the waters
rushed faster and faster with a horrid sucking sound.

Now the medicine stick fell with increasing speed, and into
the great hole went trunks of trees and tangled roots and the white
scum of the raging shore. The swirl of the waters went over the
toes of the Indian, then around his ankles, then over his knees.
At that instant a terrible head with eyes that glowed like yellow
saucers appeared in the very center of the dark whirlpool, and a
long, snakelike body coiled round and round with the water's rush.

"What do you want?" hissed Matchi Manitou, the evil one.

"Health, wealth, power, and happiness," replied the Indian.

"Then get all four from the Great Spirit," answered the evil
one, "for He gives happiness with the other three only to those who
toil in their brothers' service."

"But I wish health and wealth and power and happiness without toil," continued the Indian.

"Health and wealth and power I can give you without toil." said the evil one, "but not happiness."

"Let it be so, then," cried the Indian. "Give me health and wealth and power even if I miss happiness."

"You have spoken," hissed the evil one. "Take from between my teeth this blood-red ball. In it is all that you desire. As long as you keep it in your turtle medicine bag, you will not want any of the three, but remember, in pay, I take each year one of your best beloved things."

Instantly the head of the great beast sank out of sight, and the swirling hole became nothing but water tumbling on the shore.

The wicked Indian went back to his tepee. His wife lay dead upon the ground from the terror she had felt. Already the evil one had taken pay, but the Indian did not mind. His thoughts were too full of all that he was about to do.

In the days that followed a strange change came over him. He grew strong and straight. He became a mighty hunter. He slew his enemies with his terrible tomahawk. He robbed his neighbors of their goods and became the most powerful though the most hated ruler on the shores of the great lake; but each year, at the time of the great storm, some cherished treasure was snatched away. Now it was a daughter, and now a son, and now a white horse, until, at last, there was left nothing that he loved but a sickly young son.

The great storm came in the early fall and the youngster was blown over a cliff and killed. The wicked Indian was lying on his furs at the moment listening to the drums of the great waves. Suddenly he heard them speaking the words of Matchi Manitou.

"Come! Come! Come! Come!" they thundered over and over.

The Indian sprang up and took the red ball out of his medicine case. It turned to powder in his fingers. With a cry, he ran down to the shore of the thundering lake. The water came swirling to his feet. The great hole appeared and out of it thrust up the terrible head, with yellow saucer-like eyes.

"Your last beloved thing is dead," said the evil one. "You have nothing more to give. Now I demand yourself."

At the words, the water twisted up and over and around the Indian's knees, then around his waist, then over his head, and with a vast sucking sound, whirled him round and round and dragged him head first into the great swirling hole.

—JOSEPH BURKE EGAN

How a Devil Danced to Death
A Liberian Folktale

A devil wandered through the forest until he came to a place where two big roads crossed. There he built himself a little house. This was a bad thing for the people who used these roads, for devils are wicked and devour human beings.

When anyone came to the cross-roads, the devil would jump out of his house on the corner, holding a drum under his arm. He would beat the drum and command the wayfarer to dance.

"Dance, O Man! Dance and I will play the drum for you. He who tires first must die!"

The unfortunate traveller, whether he was a man, woman or child, would be obliged to dance a Dance of Death, for invariably the dancer tired first and was killed and eaten by the devil.

Men know that twins often have unusual powers. They make fine magicians and medicine men. They are wise in telling fortunes and know the use of herbs and poison. A pair of twins decided they would outwit and kill the devil who had killed many people from

52

their town. They left their town one morning to see what they could do. One of them crept ahead very softly and hid behind an anthill close to the devil's house. Then his brother boldly approached singing a pleasant song.

The devil heard him coming and jumped from his house. "Ho!" he cried in great delight. He had not seen a man for days. "Ho, young man! Come and dance for me!" The devil began beating excitedly on his drum.

"Thank you, sir," said the lad. "It is a fine morning for a dance. Play on!"

The devil threw back his head and laughed at such insolence. "Do you know, youth, that the one of us who tires first must die?"

"Fine," said the twin. "That means the other one will live." He danced and danced to the devil's drumming or playing. When he was tired, he skipped behind the anthill and his brother skipped out in his place. In this fashion the twins danced for three whole days; whenever one was dancing, the other one was resting. The devil was astonished to see, as he thought, one person dance on and on, day and night and he himself grew tired. The twins continued to change places. The devil dropped, wilted and at last he fell exhausted on the ground.

The twins killed the devil by cutting his body into two parts. They impaled one half on a stake and carried it into town. There it stayed as a warning to all devils that twins lived in that place and would tolerate no wicked devil tricks.

—A. DORIS BANKS HENRIES

The People of the Night
A Hawaiian Tale

The people were afraid. They did not dare go into the hills for wood nor tend their flocks out of sight of the village. They stayed behind closed doors at night and breathed freely only when the sun peeped over the great, smoking hills. The Ponaturi were abroad: queer, misshapen, evil spirits, whispering, whispering evil things; setting neighbor against neighbor with evil lies; stirring up strife between brothers in the same house by dangling wonderful necklaces of shell and, in every other evil way, trying to destroy the happiness of mankind.

Ta-Whaki looked on with sad eyes, for he was a noble youth. "The Ponaturi," said he to his brother, "must be destroyed. They go forth at night and slay and burn and stir up strife. We must find where they hide during the hours when the eye of the sun is upon them. It may happen that finding them, the great sun will aid us to destroy them."

So saying, Ta-Whaki and his brother Kariki started out along the white beach to find the lair of the Ponaturi. All day they traveled and all night, and in the dawn of the second day came to a thatched hut that stood on a high bank overlooking the sea. Before the hut sat an old woman. Her head was in her hands and she wept, the salt tears running down through her wrinkled fingers making round spots on the smooth sand between her feet.

"Old mother," said Ta-Whaki, "why do you weep?"

"I weep," said the old woman, "because I must sit here all night and warn the Ponaturi of the coming of the dawn. They come here to sleep after their mischief is done in the world, but at the first peep of the sun they hurry away to the land under the sea; for, like all evil things, they cannot live in the open day."

"Mother," said Ta-Whaki, "we have come to destroy the Ponaturi."

"Alas!" cried the woman, "that cannot be. Only the sun can destroy them, and they are too shrewd to let him catch them. You will only be killed and eaten by these terrible creatures."

"Nevertheless," said Ta-Whaki, "we shall hide in the deep thatch of the roof and see what can be done."

The two brothers spent the rest of the day gathering soft moss in the woods and piling it behind the house. When night came, they stood before the old lady. "Would you be free of the evil spirits?" they asked.

And she answered, "Oh, yes! I would gladly be free."

"Then," said Ta-Whaki, "you must sit as before and when the Ponaturi call out to you asking about the dawn you are to say, 'Sleep on, sleep on! I will call you at the right time.' Now mark you well, old mother, the right time for them is when I shall say the word and not an instant before."

So saying, Ta-Whaki and his brother hid themselves in the

thatch, just as the Ponaturi came rushing in through the doorway. The evil spirits were so tired out after their evening of terrible doings that they threw themselves down at once and fell fast asleep. When not an eye watched nor an ear listened, the brothers slipped out of the thatch and began plugging up all the holes in the hut with soft moss. All night they worked and every now and then they heard one of the Ponaturi cry out:

"Old woman, has the dawn come?" And each time they heard the old woman say, "Sleep on! Sleep on! I will call you at the right time."

Just as the sun touched the peak of the hut the Ponaturi called out again, "Old woman, has the dawn come?" and once again the old woman lulled them to sleep by saying, "Sleep on! Sleep on! I will call you at the right time." When the sun was an hour high, its light crept down from the top of the hut to the straw sides, and once again the old woman lulled them to sleep by saying, "Sleep on! Sleep on! I will call you at the right time."

Very soon the light of the sun was white and hot on the side of the hut. "Now," whispered Ta-Whaki to the old lady, "is the right time to call them."

Just at that moment the Ponaturi called out, "The side of the hut grows warm! Old woman, has the dawn come?"

And the old woman answered, "Yes, yes, it is time to get up!"

As she said the words, the brothers ran rapidly around the hut pulling out the plugs of moss. Through each hole in the wall a dagger of clear light darted so swiftly that the Ponaturi could not dodge out of its way. Screams of rage and loud wails and cries for help came from within. Then all became still as death. Ta-Whaki strode to the door and threw it open. Behold! The Ponaturi were all dead, pierced through and through by the sharp lances of the light.

You may be sure there was great rejoicing in the village. Ta-Whaki and his brother wore scarlet hibiscus flowers in their black hair and the old woman was given a seat at the right hand of the chief.

Then Ta-Whaki rose. "The Ponaturi died," he said, "when the lances of the sun struck them; so shall all evil die when the lances of the truth are cast by the strong hands of just men."

—JOSEPH BURKE EGAN

The Ride-by-Nights

Up on their brooms the Witches stream,
Crooked and black in the crescent's gleam;
One foot high, and one foot low,
Bearded, cloaked, and cowled, they go.
'Neath Charlie's wane they twitter and tweet,
And away they swarm 'neath the Dragon's feet.
With a whoop and a flutter they swing and sway,
And surge pell-mell down the Milky Way.
Betwixt the legs of the glittering Chair
They hover and squeak in the empty air.
Then round they swoop past the glimmering Lion
To where Sirius barks behind huge Orion;
Up, then, and over to wheel amain,
Under the silver, and home again.

—WALTER DE LA MARE

Witches, Wizards, Soothsayers—
the Occult

Long ago, when most people knew nothing about medicine or science, they thought sickness and misfortune were caused by spells cast by wicked witches, wizards, magicians, or evil spirits. When someone died, others often disguised themselves so as not to be recognized and thus cursed with the disease. One way they disguised themselves was by painting their bodies with stripes.

Often each small clan or tribe had a medicine man, shaman, or tribal priest who used magic words and spells to chase away sickness or bad luck. Sometimes these men used healing herbs and soothing drinks which they alone knew about, and from some early remedies useful medicines developed. Even today wise and kind medicine men sometimes teach doctors about diseases and their cure.

Most medicine men, shamans, or tribal priests had power over primitive people and were thought to be magicians who knew much that was occult, or secret and hidden. In treating a disease they often used weird, supposedly magic and occult ceremonies.

Often these magicians were asked to make bad magic to destroy someone's enemy or a tribal foe. They would then perhaps make a small wax or clay figure to represent the enemy and stick thorns or other sharp things into it so the enemy would suffer in the places pierced. Similarly, some people today stick pins into voodoo dolls to spite or harm someone else. Many people today are fascinated by the ancient ideas of magic and the occult, and practice them.

When the tribal magician wished to help a person or tribe, he made good, sympathetic magic. Before hunting tigers, the hunter might get from the magic-maker the tooth of a tiger killed in a previous hunt. After the magician used magic words and motions over it, the hunter wore it as a charm or amulet to give him the tiger's speed, courage, and cunning, and to protect him from its teeth and claws.

As tribes grew into city-states or nations, these medicine men or tribal priests often regulated religion and were thought to have magic power and ability to foretell the future. For instance, in ancient Rome and other places, seers, soothsayers or interpreters studied the flight of birds or examined animals' livers and then told people what was about to happen and what was best to do. Ancient Romans called such men augurers or diviners. They did not practice witchcraft, for witchcraft seeks to control the future and people by magic or occult means, whereas augurers claimed to foretell the future. Nevertheless, many people then, as today, were so bound by old fears that they relied heavily on the augurers' fortune-telling and on witchcraft.

Still others were amused by such practices. They agreed with the Roman statesman Cato, who, more than 2,000 years ago, said that after he watched augurers studying animals' insides and other omens, he did not know how one augurer could look at another without laughing.

So it is today—countless people are not interested in having their fortunes told and their future predicted, while numbers of others consult soothsayers or fortune-tellers as ancient peoples did. Astrologers were very important in Babylonia thousands of years ago, and many of their practices spread to Europe. Some have been revived recently in many lands, especially that of casting horoscopes. Since ancient times many people have been afraid of doing anything before finding out what their horoscopes read, what was "in the stars" for them.

Through horoscope-casting many astrologers grew rich and powerful while those who consulted them remained dependent and confused. Some sincere astrologers of long ago, however, were becoming astronomers whose discoveries advanced mankind's knowledge of the universe.

Since most early religions worshiped nature in its many forms, tribal seers or tribal priests often directed nature festivals. Among the Celts who lived in much of what is now called France and in parts of the British Isles, Druid priests were powerful. For several centuries, ending during the first century A.D., they kept order among the people, tried and punished criminals, and conducted religious ceremonies.

To them the oak tree was sacred. So was mistletoe growing on an oak, and they cut it with golden sickles amid great ceremony. Druid priests foretold the future, much as Roman augurers did. Often the way a sacrificed animal or person writhed in the fire was supposed to give these priest-magicians special knowledge. Grim tales have come down about Druid human sacrifices and the cruel ways in which those who did not cooperate were put to death.

Druid priests were thought to control the weather by magic. As in many other nature religions, the worshipers expected the priest-magician to use magic against the mysterious forces of nature. During an eclipse, for instance, terrified people depended on the priests to fight the darkness and bring back the sun's light and warmth.

From some such beginnings came the idea of wizards—men who were thought to hold magic power over nature and persons. Others believed to hold mysterious powers were sometimes called sorcerers or conjurers or necromancers. Some wizards were thought to be able to make things appear and disappear, even to change their own or another person's shape. Some people believed these dealers in magic knew secret words which, when said at exactly the right moment, could produce a variety of changes. *Abracadabra,* a very old Latin word, was one of those supposed to have magic power.

In ancient times kings often asked wizards for advice and many legends are told of their powers. The legends about King Arthur include the tale of the wizard Merlin, who caused the appearance of the stone with the magic sword which only Arthur was able to draw and thus become king.

From Finland's legends, recounted in the epic poem "Kalevala," the story of Vainaimonen tells how he made magic. The "Kalevala" tells also of Vainaimonen's brother Ilmarinen, the wonder-smith who forged the magic mill, called Sampo, which produced from its three sides salt, meal and money.

Tales are told in many lands, and often the same tale spreads from one country to another, of wizard wonder-smiths who made magic at their forges. It was natural for the smith to be considered a wonder-worker for many of his creations involved metal—and it was not unusual for a smith to attempt to turn other metals into gold.

Some early chemists and scientists were called wizards for they were gathering, bit by bit and often in secret, startling information about science, medicine, chemistry, and the universe. During the Middle Ages some of them were thought to use magic and were called alchemists. In the city of Prague, toward the end of the sixteenth century, Emperor Rudolf II built, close to his castle, a street called Alchemists' Street.

There was in Prague, the capital of Bohemia, a great community of Jews who had come there after persecution in other countries. The Great Rabbi Löw was a wise, kind, and brave leader of Jews not only in Bohemia but in many lands. He risked his life so that Jews would be allowed to stay in Prague. Simple and sincerely humble in his manner, this great man had a special genius for understanding people. He had deep insights into what was hidden or occult in the spiritual world. Although he said that all magic was wicked unless it meant the preventing through prayer of an evil destiny, many legends grew about the rabbi as a magic maker. He lived in an age when much thought was influenced by the cabala, that mysterious system of finding the meanings of life through the Scriptures by use of mystic combinations of numbers.

There are many stories from various lands of how persons brought to life a statue or clay figure, sometimes called a golem, but none are more numerous than the stories of Rabbi Löw's golem which was made to serve him in many amazing ways as he tried to protect his people from persecution. The golem was created for good work and did not function unless there was placed in its forehead or under its tongue a "Shem," a paper containing a combination of letters denoting one of the names of God.

One legend tells that although Rabbi Löw had insisted the golem was to be used only for the common good of the people and their religion, and not for personal secular services, the rabbi's wife once ordered the golem to fill two water kegs in the kitchen. The golem kept bringing pails and pails of water from the brook until the water overflowed into the courtyard. Rabbi Löw's wife was terrified but she could find no way to stop the golem. And then the rabbi himself came home, discovered the mischief, and was able to give the right orders which caused the golem to set down the pails. Perhaps from such a legend came the tale of "The Sorcerer's Apprentice," included in this book, for Rabbi Löw's fame as a wonder-worker of great wisdom spread far and wide. His was the unselfish magic that benefitted countless people.

Rabbi Löw was interested also in invention and is said to have shown the emperor pictures projected on the wall of a dark room. This is believed by some to have been the beginning of the magic lantern.

Through the ages people often have been frightened by the so-called magicians and wizards, although some of them, like Rabbi Löw, have tried to discover more of the wonderful mysteries of the universe and to use what they have learned for the good of mankind. Perhaps some readers of this book will work to find ways to bring the hidden treasures of this universe to good use for all people or through their "wizardry" will make useful inventions. Always there will be mysteries, hidden for ages, waiting for unselfish "wizards" to solve and bring greater happiness and freedom to people.

(Witches and Witchcraft)

Always everywhere sorcery and witchcraft have frightened many people and attracted others. More than 3,000 years ago, when

Hebrew slaves in Egypt were freed some took with them to the new homeland ancient fears and superstitions about magic; and they found among their new neighbors in Canaan some of the same attitudes about sorcery and the occult.

Eager to free people from the power of sorcerers, the great liberator Moses and other lawmakers decreed that wizards and witches should not be allowed to live. And in the ancient Babylonian Code of Hammurabi sorcery was condemned. Despite such laws, countless people all over the world have tried to solve problems, fears, or loneliness by turning to witches or sorcerers for help or escape. And many persons, today as through the centuries, have claimed to be witches of special occult power.

The increase of witchcraft often happens at a time when great, new discoveries are being made, or when thousands of people are moving to places strange to them; or when old ideas and customs and religious beliefs crumble and new ones come to light. This is so in our time when discoveries in space, science, and medicine, together with religious changes, leave many people amazed and insecure. Today, too, many are moving from place to place, leaving behind them the security of families and old friends.

In Europe several hundred years ago, during the end of the Middle Ages and the beginning of the Renaissance, thousands of people were insecure and frightened. Ideas about the size of the world were changing fast—the news spread around Europe that the navigator Columbus had visited a whole new world across the ocean. With the compass gaining in general use, seamen grew more daring all the time.

Scholars from the East were coming to Europe to teach much old knowledge of which many Europeans had never heard. Some of them wanted to explore this newly discovered knowledge; some were shaken by it. After the invention of movable type for the printing press, more books were printed. Most books helped people advance in their thinking, but others offered witchcraft to confused people as an escape from a quickly-changing world.

Questions about religious beliefs shook many people. Some lost their former faith and retreated into witchcraft and the nature religions. With so many ideas and situations changing throughout most of their lives, people often became rebellious. Some rioted and tried to break down everything. Many were lonely and scared.

Frightful tales are told about witches in those fast-changing times. It is wrong, though, to judge harshly what people did at any time in history because their thinking and actions were influenced by new and often erroneous ideas. Often the bad, instead of the good, things are talked about most and remembered. And old books reveal that during those times, as in our own, it was the fad to talk about everything that was wrong with the world. Some people were afraid to speak of happy things fearing others would think them odd.

The witchcraft craze spread through Europe during those disturbed times at the end of the Middle Ages and the beginning of our present era in history. Usually a witch was thought to be an old hag who lived alone, whose only friends were other witches, devils, wizards or warlocks. Sometimes a witch was young and beautiful and could cast a spell very easily. Witches were said to get magic power from the devil. Women who claimed to be witches brewed a "flying ointment" which they sniffed and rubbed on their bodies, declaring that it made them able to fly around the air.

Doctors have found that some of these flying ointments contained drugs that caused weird sensations and hallucinations and drugs that changed heart action so the users felt they were going through space. A witch might take such a drug "trip" alone or with other witches. Often they stuffed keyholes and other places through which the drug fumes might escape or through which good spirits might enter. Then they rubbed themselves with the drug mixture, sniffed greedily, and sometimes sipped the brew. Off they'd go on a trip to escape reality and dream of fantastic experiences.

Sometimes, instead of staying indoors after beginning their trip they snatched up brooms, distaffs, or rakes and dashed outdoors, "flying" to meet the devil on one of the witch hills. One famous witch hill was the Brocken in the Hartz Mountains of Germany. As witches sped along they often screamed curses on ordinary people and stopped to cast a spell on families against whom they had a grudge.

Although witches usually lived alone, occasionally they lived in a "coven" which might have thirteen members. Sometimes among the members were young girls learning to be witches. Today there are many such covens where people have special rites and share secret ceremonies. Witches often gathered in a mystical circle for secret, occult ceremonies, danced weird dances, then used flying ointment to take them on a trip.

A witch was thought to have a "familiar," a bewitched animal like a toad, bat, frog, lizard, or goat, through which she talked with the spirit world or worked her witchcraft. A black cat was believed to have special, evil power when used by a witch. Thousands of years ago in Greece a bird called a jynx was used in witchcraft; and to this day people speak of being "jinxed" when they have bad luck. Today, too, some people who say they are witches claim that a cat or other small animal is their "familiar.

For centuries it was thought that a person could be bewitched and changed for a time into one of many animals, including a werewolf. Frightening werewolves roamed at night, bewitched, but at the first light of day were changed back to people. Besides changing people into beasts, witches were said to cast spells that could make a person sleep many years. Usually the spell was broken when some brave person performed a kind, unselfish, loving deed for the bewitched. Many old folktales and fairy stories, such as "Snow White," "Sleeping Beauty," and "Beauty and the Beast" tell of how the spell was broken by the courage and kindness of another person.

In Homer's ancient Greek story-poem, the *Odyssey*, a beautiful sorceress, Circe, changed Odysseus' companions into swine; but he bravely went to save them with no thought for his own safety. Luckily, he met the kind god Hermes who gave him an herb that would protect him. So Odysseus and his men were saved.

Sometimes people tried to break the magic power by cutting the long hair of a witch or wizard, since their long hair was thought to help them perform their bad magic. All over the world all sorts of charms and magic rites have been used against witches, wizards, and other sorcerers and evil spirits.

Iron was thought to be powerful against their magic, and a horseshoe protected against evil spells and brought good luck. One reason for this was that horseshoes are forged by a blacksmith, and many folktales tell of wonder-working smiths who help people. Also, because of its crescent shape a horseshoe is a symbol of the new moon, and the moon is connected with magic. Horseshoes were hung on barns to guard against witches and evil spirits who might bring disease to animals or ride the horses wildly at night. Sometimes persons trusted the healing charm of three horseshoes nailed to a sick child's bed, instead of giving the child medical care.

From ancient Roman times iron nails or spikes were driven into house walls to drive away a plague of sickness. In parts of the British Isles, to cure a toothache the gum was scratched with a new nail and then the nail was driven into an oak tree. As protection against witches, demons, and wicked fairies, nails were driven into wooden bedsteads. Sometimes groups of people held an annual nail-driving, or "spiking," when a spike was driven into a wall to cure sicknesses of those present. Such spiking has come back into use by various people today. Other ways of protection against witches, sorcerers, devils, and such were to stick pins in the doorpost or to keep a jar of pins under the hearthstone.

Sometimes witches were called on to harm someone. They often cast a spell as they stuck pins in an image of the one to be hurt, much as wizards and other sorcerers did. Not more than 400 years ago in Europe witches were hired to mix poison to kill someone's enemy or make him go insane.

Witches and sorcerers were thought to know more than other persons, especially about drugs, magic, and the mysteries of life. The word "witch" originally came from the word "wicca," meaning "wise" or "wise one" or "sorcerer." "Wicca" was connected with a very old form of nature worship, and from ancient times people met in country places to hold rites in honor of the nature and fertility gods. The wise one was thought to have a special ability to control forces of nature, often through making a sacrifice in a mystic way.

Some of these very ancient witchcraft customs have come down through the centuries, and most people now think of them only as good luck charms. For instance, for many years farmers in Europe made a "corn dolly," which was a very intricately twisted bundle of the very last of the grain, to be brought in with ceremony at harvest time. This dolly was hung in the house or barn to ensure a good harvest the next year.

Naturally, since it was thought that special secret, occult knowledge and craft were necessary to induce this continuance of life, the wise ones, including witches and sorcerers, took a prominent place in nature festivals, even long after pagan fertility cults seemed to have ended in Europe.

At times witches held wild revels which were called Witches' Sabbaths, or Sabbats. Unlike the Sabbaths of Jews or Christians, these were more like the Sabbaths of ancient Babylonia, when people were afraid of angry, evil demonic gods. The Babylonian god Bel and countless other gods demanded to be appeased with special rites, gifts, and sacrifices. Some accounts of Witches' Sabbaths say that only witches, sorcerers, and demons came to these awful nighttime musters and worshiped the Devil and under his direction planned evil work. Some accounts say that many other people who still followed ancient nature religions traveled to witches' gatherings and took part in superstitious rituals. Many became enslaved by the evil power of the witches' drugs, and became unable to tell right from wrong. Often they joined in a frenzied orgy.

Today, in many countries, people are returning to ancient "earth" or nature religions. Some are led by persons who claim to be witches or wizards gifted in witchcrafts. Some turn to Satan worship or demon worship.

In various times and places the Devil (or Satan) was said to be a tireless fiddler whose music lured people to dance until they were bewitched or dropped dead. Witches were said to bring young people whom they were training as helpers to meet the Devil, hear his music, join in the excitement, and give themselves to the Devil. A number of lonely, unhappy, or bored young people were attracted to witches to learn magic, get power over other people, and escape from everyday life with drugs. They gave up the religion of the church and joined nature cults with secret ceremonies, superstitions, and often degrading or cruel practices.

Naturally, church leaders were distressed by the witch mania sweeping through Europe toward the end of the Middle Ages. In 1484, to try to protect people from heresy connected with witchcraft, the Pope wrote a decree against it and sent out agents on witchhunts. A few years later one such agent said that he alone had burned 900 witches.

Nevertheless, witchcraft spread. The Spanish Inquisition tried to stamp it out by banning the numerous books that dealt with it and necromancy. Everywhere people were urged to report witches in their area so they could be brought to trial.

Old pictures show mass burning of accused "witches" in Germany. In France, at Toulouse 400 were killed in a single execution, and in the city of Treves alone 7,000 were killed. All over southern Europe, a great number of persons accused of being witches were tortured and killed.

Because so many people were terrified of witches, many innocent persons were accused falsely and killed. Neighbors accused others of being witches—to pay back a grudge, or to put the blame for their failure on having been "bewitched," or to share in the property that was seized from the so-called witch.

For centuries many women had gathered herbs and mixed home remedies for their families and neighbors. Now, thousands of innocent women were accused of poisoning or bewitching people or cattle and of working with demons or the Devil. Not only were women killed as witches, but so were many other innocent people including children, farmers, clergymen, and men of all ages.

To add to the general distress and fear, Europe had been torn by war for many years, and sick or wounded soldiers wandered, often spreading sickness and plague. Sometimes old women or other persons who knew about healing medicines took pity on these sick men who were far from home or homeless. A person who tried to heal a sick enemy soldier might be accused of witchcraft and working with the Devil to aid the country's enemy.

All church leaders tried to protect people from the Devil's power. During those years the church in Europe was divided, and several churches were established which did not acknowledge the Pope as their head. Some of their leaders, also, carried on witch hunts. It is estimated that in Europe during the 250 years stretching from the late 1400s to about 1782 approximately 300,000 persons were executed for the supposed practice of witchcraft.

King James I of England greatly feared demons and witches, and thought they caused terrible storms, especially at sea. Also, he was afraid they would lead people into wicked, rebellious ways. So he wrote a book about demons. More than 300 years old, this book may be seen in Oxford, England, at the famous Bodleian Library where there are other valuable and historic books.

As head of the Church of England, King James felt it his duty to make the church strong and protect his subjects by keeping them loyal to it. When they disagreed or dissented with church teachings it was thought they were in the power of the Devil or of evil spirits, or were bewitched, and they were called heretics. Also, they were considered wicked if they did not obey the law that said they must attend the national church. So King James hunted down such heretics, together with thousands of "witches" and sorcerers.

Among the refugees who fled from England were the Pilgrims who, in time, settled in America. As various new colonists came to America from Europe they brought a fear of witches, for all Europe had set the example of witch hunts. Many, many thousands were being killed in Spain and other southern European countries. And it is estimated that during the 87-year lifetime of John Alden, who came to Plymouth in 1620, 40,000 "witches" had been killed in

England. Yet, the Pilgrims of Plymouth never killed a witch, and a woman there was fined and whipped for accusing another of being a witch.

In the rest of Massachusetts, however, many colonists who held the old-world beliefs that witches were possessed by the Devil tried to rid their communities of such wicked creatures. Some New England clergymen promoted witch trials and tried to stamp out heresy. In Connecticut several "witches" were killed, including two as late as 1650. During the Salem, Massachusetts, witch hunts nineteen persons were killed.

The witch-hunt frenzy ended in New England in 1696 when Judge Samuel Sewall bravely stood with bowed head in Old South Meeting House, Boston, while his confession of shame for having taken part in Salem witch trials was read. Later the jurymen, also, said they had done wrong. Judge Sewall's name is famous for helping New England people come to their senses about witch trials.

Although after 1696 witch hunts were frowned on in New England, many people there and elsewhere still feared witches. In Virginia, witches had been punished. And in New Jersey, in Salem County, a "witch" was killed in the early 1700s. She was accused of having bewitched a man and a boy to murder the Lord High Sheriff, James Sherron. Many German settlers in Pennsylvania and other areas put hex signs on barns and houses and used charms and magic words and ceremonies to protect their farms.

It was natural that people of many nationalities who came to America to settle should bring the fear of witches. Even today in all sorts of places, including remote valleys and big cities, a variety of people blame witches for misfortunes, or else they try to practice witchcraft.

Among many Indians of North America, fear and suspicion of

sorcerers prevailed and often made them hate their medicine men. Sometimes they killed a medicine man who failed in a cure. The Mojaves of the Southwest thought the medicine man killed so he would have a large band of souls in his power in afterlife. Instead of killing the patient with weapons, he frightened the patient with sorcery so he could not get well. In time, though, different tribes threw off many ancient fears and moved forward with new understanding.

Little by little, Europeans and their descendants cast off the fear of witchcraft and sorcery. But still many colonists to the new world brought age-old inherited fears. In the little island of Bermuda, for instance, records show that witches were killed as late as 1664. (*The False Ebony Tree* by Terry Tucker, published by the Bermuda Historical Society, refers to witch executions there.) The last recorded execution of a witch in Europe was in Scotland in 1722, but this did not necessarily stop the denouncement and persecution of so-called witches.

Spooky tales of witches and uncanny happenings were told continually. For instance, in the Berlin Mountains across the Hudson from Albany, New York, a farmer could tell that his horse had been driven all night because its tail and mane were braided in witch fashion and it was tired all day. One midnight he discovered a big black cat on the horse's back, and he stuck a three-tined pitch-fork into the cat's back. The next day an old woman who lived on the farm was sick, and the doctor found three deep wounds in her back. This is but one of the well-known witch tales of persons changed into animals at night.

Everywhere there were instructions or recipes for becoming a witch, one from Schenectady being to stand on a manure heap at midnight, waving a red lantern behind your back with your left hand while looking at the moon over your right shoulder. Another instruction was to say the Lord's Prayer backward very fast three times with feet and hands crossed.

Even in ancient times, however, not all people believed in witchcraft and sorcery. In many places in the world persons came to realize that magic rites and incantations did not bring the results for which they were planned. It was as if those who relied on magic were trying to pull strings to which nothing was attached, for the rain still fell and the sun shone by day and the moon by night. Seasons followed each other with seedtime and harvest, warmth and cold.

In Europe during the sixteenth and seventeeth centuries some important persons from various churches and synagogues kept speaking and writing against the cruelty and folly of witch hunts.

A few hundred years ago some leading doctors said that many persons thought to be witches were to be pitied and cared for because their minds were unbalanced. Such medical opinions and advice, along with horrible memories of what had been done to thousands of persons falsely accused, slowly stirred people's consciences to take better care of troubled persons.

Always there will be some people who seem to see more deeply into the mysterious and the occult, and some who have the power of influencing others in a way hard to explain. Fear of being bewitched still persists among some people, although millions have shaken off this ancient fear. No longer, either, do most people think that witches, wizards, or demons cause storms or eclipses. Instead they try to prepare for the storm, or get equipment to watch an eclipse. Instead of fearing the evil spirits of disease, grown-ups and even young children throughout the world are learning more about how to combat disease and promote good health, and are trying to improve the environment.

—MILDRED CORELL LUCKHARDT

The Sorcerer's Apprentice

Long ago and far away, in a dark, mysterious room an old sorcerer worked his magic with many secret spells and incantations. He had for a helper a boy apprentice who was sworn to secrecy, never to reveal any of the magic to another person. The apprentice tended the fire over which magic potions were heated; he gathered herbs and stones the wizard wanted; he ran errands of all sorts. One of his duties was to carry water from the river to fill the tub.

Whenever the boy was in the room with the master sorcerer, even when sweeping the floor the boy watched and listened to all the magic words that could cast spells. He kept hoping for the day when the old man might leave him alone for awhile with charms, potions, magic formulas. "Then," said the apprentice to himself. "I shall make magic, too. No more common work for me!"

At last, one day the sorcerer went out! He called from the doorway, "While I am gone, carry water from the river to fill the tub." Then he was gone.

Immediately, the boy began his sorcery. He'd get that water
carried from the river by magic. The broomstick would do the work!
Full of excitement because of his new power, he spoke the magic
words that he had learned from the sorcerer, then called to the broom
standing by the door,

> "Ho, thou battered broomstick! Take ye
> This seedy coat and wear it—
> Ha, thou household drudge I'll make ye
> Do my bidding; ay, and fear it!"

Putting legs and a head on the broomstick, he shouted

> "To the river there, now
> Bear the pail at once!
> Hear ye! hear ye!
> Hence! your spritely
> Office rightly,
> Featly showing!
> Toil, until with water clear, ye
> Fill the bath to overflowing."

Carrying the bucket, the broomstick clattered downhill to the
river while the apprentice watched, delighted with his success as a
magician. The bucket flashed in the stream and came out brimful of
water. Back up the hill came the broomstick with the water and threw
it into the tub. Back and forth, back and forth it went, faster, faster,
while the boy watched from the doorway, very proud of the spell he
had cast with the right magic words. Again and again the spellbound
broomstick carried water to the tub.

Suddenly the apprentice felt water running over his feet. He
dashed to the tub. It was overflowing, and the floor was becoming a
lake. Still the broomstick kept bringing buckets of water, like a goblin or kobold bent on malicious mischief. The boy frantically tried

to remember the magic words to break the spell, but he could not. He yelled to the broomstick to stop, but it kept bringing water. As the water rose higher, the apprentice kept yelling for it to stop. Then he threatened to cut it in two with the hatchet if it didn't stop. But the water kept rising higher and higher.

The boy was terrified of the goblin he had made. He swung the hatchet and split the Thing in two. With great relief he cried,

"Now I move securely,
And I breathe again!"

But no! The two halves of the broomstick became goblins with buckets, and rushed back and forth carrying more water from the river. As the boy shrieked for the master sorcerer's help, the man came in. Seeing the water rushing through the hall and on the stairs, he immediately spoke the magic words to break the spell. The water poured out the door and down the hill, while the sorcerer said

"Broom, avaunt thee!
To thy nook there!
Lie, thou spook, there!
Only answer,
When for mine own ends I want thee,
I, the master necromancer!"

The ballad "The Sorcerer's Apprentice" was written by the famous German poet Johann Wolfgang von Goethe, who was born in 1749. During the past 200 years this ballad has been translated into many languages and set to music by various composers. One famous musical setting was composed by the Frenchman, Paul Dukas. People in many lands enjoy listening to this music and recalling the story of the apprentice who made more magic than he could control.

—ADAPTED BY MILDRED CORELL LUCKHARDT

Witches' Song

Early, early, comes the dark,
something moves along the ditches.
Was that singing? Hark, oh, hark
to the chanting of the witches!

Come, sisters, come
let us screech at the windows,
let us blow out the candles
and breathe on their hair,

we've shadowed the moon
and called up the night-wind,
the owl and the cat and the broom
will be there.

Let us turn their blood chill
with the sight of our faces,
let us touch them with fingers
both crooked and cold,

and then shrilly laughing
we'll be off to the hill tops
to frisk and to frolic
as always of old.

Did you hear them? Were they saying
scary things to shake the knees?
Or was that but breezes playing
in the dry and brittle trees?

—ELIZABETH COATSWORTH

The Horned Woman
Irish Folktale

A rich woman sat up late one night carding and preparing wool while all the family and servants were asleep. Suddenly a knock was given at the door, and a voice called out "Open! Open!"

"Who is there?" said the woman of the house.

"I am the Witch of the One Horn," was answered.

The mistress, supposing that one of her neighbors had called and required assistance, opened the door and a woman entered, having in her hand a pair of wool carders, and bearing a horn on her forehead, as if growing there. She sat down by the fire in silence, and began to card the wool with violent haste. Suddenly she paused, and said aloud, "Where are the women? They delay too long."

Then a second knock came to the door, and a voice called as before, "Open! Open!"

The mistress felt herself constrained to rise and open to the call, and immediately a second witch entered, having two horns on her forehead, and in her hand a wheel for spinning wool.

81

"Give me place," she said. "I am the Witch of the Two Horns," and she began to spin as quick as lightning. And so the knocks came on, and the call was heard and the witches entered, until at last twelve women sat round the fire—the first with one horn, the last with twelve horns.

And they carded the thread and turned their spinning wheels, and wound and wove.

All were singing together an ancient rhyme, but no word did they speak to the mistress of the house. Strange to hear and frightful to look upon were these twelve women, with their horns and their wheels; and the mistress felt near to death, and she tried to rise that she might call for help, but she could not move, nor could she uttter a word or a cry, for the spell of the witches was upon her.

Then one of them called to her in Irish, and said, "Rise, woman, and make us a cake."

Then the mistress searched for a vessel to bring water from the well that she might mix the meal and make the cake but she could find none.

And they said to her, "Take a sieve, and bring water in it."

And she took the sieve, and went to the well; but the water poured from it, and she could fetch none for the cake, and she sat down by the well and wept.

Then came a voice by her, and said, "Take yellow clay and moss and bind them together, and plaster the sieve so that it will hold."

This she did, and the sieve held the water for the cake and the voice said again, "Return, and when thou comest to the north angle of the house cry aloud three times, and say, 'The mountain of the Fenian women and the sky over it is all on fire!"

And she did so.

When the witches inside heard the call, a great and terrible cry broke from their lips, and they rushed forth with wild lamentations and shrieks, and fled away to Slievenamon, where was their chief abode. But the Spirit of the Well bade the mistress of the house enter and prepare her home against the enchantments of the witches, if they returned again.

And first, to break their spells, she sprinkled water in which she had washed her child's feet (the feet-water) outside the door on the threshold; secondly, she took the cake which the witches had made in her absence, of meal mixed with the blood drawn from the sleeping family, and she broke the cake in bits, and placed a bit in the mouth of each sleeper, and they were restored; and she took the cloth they had woven and placed it half in and half out of the chest with the padlock; and lastly, she secured the door with a great crossbeam fastened in the jambs, so that they could not enter, and having done these things she waited.

Not long were the witches in coming, and they raged and called for vengeance.

"Open! Open!" they screamed. "Open, feet-water!"

"I cannot," said the feet-water. "I am scattered on the ground, and my path is down to the Lough."

"Open, open wood and trees and beam," they cried to the door.

"I cannot," said the door, "for the beam is fixed in the jambs, and I have no power to move."

"Open, open, cake that we have made and mingled with blood!" they cried again.

"I cannot," said the cake, "for I am broken and bruised, and my blood is on the lips of the sleeping children."

Then the witches rushed through the air with great cries, and fled back to Slievenamon, uttering strange curses on the Spirit of the Well, who had wished their ruin. But the woman and the house were left in peace, and a mantle dropped by one of the witches was kept hung up by the mistress as a sign of the night's awful contest; and this mantle was in possession of the same family from generation to generation for five hundred years after.

—FROM AUGUSTA BAKER'S SELECTIONS FOR
The Talking Tree, Fairy Tales from Fifteen Lands

What the Gray Cat Sings

The Cat was once a weaver,
      A weaver, a weaver,
An old and withered weaver
      Who labored late and long;
And while she made the shuttle hum
And wove the weft and clipped the thrum,
Beside the loom with droning drum
      She sang the weaving song:
         "Pr-rrum, pr-rrum,
Thr-ree thr-reads in the thr-rum,
         Pr-rrum!"

The Cat's no more a weaver,
      A weaver, a weaver,
An old and wrinkled weaver,
      For though she did no wrong,
A witch hath changed the shape of her
That dwindled down and clothed in fur
Beside the hearth with droning purr
      She thrums her weaving song:
         "Pr-rrum, pr-rrum,
Thr-ree thr-reads in the thr-rum,
         Pr-rrum!"

—ARTHUR GUITERMAN

The Bad Kittens

You may call, you may call,
But the little black cats won't hear you,
The little black cats are maddened
By the bright green light of the moon,
They are whirling and running and hiding,
They are wild who were once so confiding,
They are crazed when the moon is riding—
You will not catch the kittens soon.
They care not for saucers of milk,
They think not of pillows of silk,
Your softest, crooningest call
Is less than the buzzing of flies.
They are seeing more than you see,
They are hearing more than you hear,
And out of the darkness they peer
With a goblin light in their eyes.

—ELIZABETH COATSWORTH

The Nick of Time

All evening the little cat had been the very model of a fireside puss. He sat on the hearthrug with his eyes shut and paws tucked underneath him, a fluffy black ball purring like a small teakettle.

Then the family went to bed.

The black puss opened eyes that gleamed a bright pale amber in the faint glimmer from the dying embers. He stretched himself long and slim and sleek.

The fire went out, but his eyes still glittered in the dark as he crossed the carpet on velvet paws. Tall and lean, he stood up on his hind legs, and with teeth and claws he pulled the window curtain aside so a moonbeam could get in.

He sat down then, but he did not look like a fluffy ball and his eyes did not close. He watched the moonbeam cross the floor slowly and begin to creep up the wall. He crouched ready.

In the very nick of time—that crack of a minute at midnight when the clock has struck one but has not yet reached twelve—the moonbeam fell full across the face of a looking glass. And, quick as the flash of light, the black cat leaped at the mirror and vanished through it.

"You've come in the nick of time, Merlin," said the Witch, looking up from the fire she was so carefully laying on a triangle of hazel twigs, witch's bane and dry nightshade leaves first and then hemlock logs over all. "I was beginning to wonder if you'd manage it this year."

"I wouldn't fail you, madam," replied the black cat. "Not on Midsummer Night."

He arched his back as bony old fingers scratched him between the shoulder blades, sending bright blue sparks out from his fur to kindle her fire.

"That's my Merlin," the Witch said with satisfaction as the flames soared and crackled. "It seems good to have your help once more. How are you making out with that family you adopted?"

"As well as could be expected," Merlin admitted. "They have a generous hand with the fish and cream and their hearthrug has a nice deep pile. Taken all in all, I have no complaints."

The hag's laugh was hoarse and scratchy as a slate pencil.

"The same old Merlin! You've always been a great one for your comforts. I was surprised, though, to hear from a passing owl that you had taken a place with children. A bit of a come-down, isn't it, after some of your lives?"

"I *like* those children," Merlin said a trifle defiantly. "Now I have got them trained, they don't hug me as Jill wanted to do at first, and Ronnie doesn't expect me to be forever jumping after spools on strings as if I were a six weeks' kitten."

The Witch was doubled up with mirth at the notion of the Merlin she knew being treated like a six weeks' kitten.

"Well," she said, wiping her eyes on a cobwebby sleeve, "I don't doubt they've discovered you have other charms and a playful nature in some respects."

"Yes, indeed," Merlin answered smugly. "I have been able to arrange several diversions for my young friends. They have come to look forward to the thirteenth, and I was sorry to disappoint them this month. But I was resting my powers against tonight."

"I am very glad you did," said the Witch.

"Besides," Merlin went on, "we must move with the times. In these modern days vacations with pay are provided for everyone, even wizards, and vacations with sardines for cats. It is one of the few signs of progress I have been able to observe in my latest life. But I must try to think up something especially entertaining for the children on the thirteenth of July."

"You will do it, too, if you put your mind to it," cackled the Witch. "I'd wager my best broomstick on that. Meanwhile, it is Midsummer Night and the hours are flitting fast."

The Witch and the black cat set about their preparations.

In the flickering firelight, the small cat whirled and twirled like the shadow of a dervish; and before the bat could squeak thrice the ancient beldame had saddled her thornwood broomstick and whistled up a wind. She twisted her magic moonstone three times widdershins to set their direction and Merlin sprang up behind her as she snatched the reins.

There was not a starprick in the night sky as they headed into the teeth of a howling gale.

Many an unfanciful traveler that Midsummer Night began to think himself bewitched when highly unreasonable accidents overtook him and he picked himself up again to the tune of wild, shrieking laughter.

And many a person who hated cats and several old enemies of the Witch's came to regret ill-considered slights and insults and injuries. Locked doors had no power to keep that pair at bay, for they had only to whistle in keyholes to open them wide.

At last they headed the broomstick down to pasture on a hilltop where other creatures of the night were celebrating the Midsummer according to their traditions. Puckish figures with high shrill voices capered madly amongst the black cocks and the black goats and the ravens and the crows in the flittering flashes of the will-o-the-wisps. And other witches and warlocks joined in weird fellowship till the cock crowed in the false dawn to send them back to their everyday lives or their farmyards, or their graves.

When the family got up in the morning, the little black cat was on the hearthrug in front of a cold grate, a fluffy black ball with his eyes shut and his paws tucked underneath him.

Mr. Saunders poked him gently in the ribs with a carpet-slippered toe on his way to the breakfast table.

"I don't see how cats can spend so much of their lives sleeping," he said. "He hasn't stirred all night, and with all that wind keeping everybody else awake, too. Did you ever hear such a gale in late June?"

Ronnie and Jill were not so sure their cat spent most of his life sleeping. As they watched him, Merlin opened and shut one eye in a deliberate wink; and he was quite wide awake when they brought him a saucer of milk.

—JOAN HOWARD

The Witches' Chant

In Shakespeare's play The Tragedy of Macbeth *is a weird chant by three witches as they mixed a horrible brew in a great caldron one gloomy night in their cave on a lonely heath in Scotland. Some weeks before that, during a thunderstorm while the three hags were making an evil charm to destroy a seaman, Macbeth and Banquo came across the heath. These two generals in the King's army were returning to their homes in triumph after putting down a rebellion against the King. At sight of the witches they asked for a prophecy about the future. Macbeth became so excited when they told of the great power he would have that he began plotting to get it at once. Indeed, the evil witches' prophecy goaded him and Lady Macbeth to murder the King and Banquo so Macbeth could become king.*

Although Macbeth and his wife became king and queen, they had no happiness because thoughts of their guilt tortured them, and they were haunted by the ghosts of the murdered. They were terrified that someone would find out what wicked things they had done. Desperate, Macbeth went to the witches' cave to beg them to prophesy his fate.

Meanwhile, the witches had been scheming with Hecate, evil Queen of Night and Witchcraft and Hades, to incite Macbeth to more violence and

*treachery so that, as a result, he would be ruined. While he crossed the
heath to their cavern they stirred foul things in the boiling cauldron.*

The Witches' Chant

First Witch.   Round about the cauldron go:
                    In the poison'd entrails throw.
                    Toad, that under cold stone
                    Days and nights has thirty one
                    Swelter'd venom sleeping got,
                    Boil thou first i' the charmed pot.

All.   Double, double toil and trouble;
                    Fire burn and cauldron bubble.

Second Witch. Fillet of a fenny snake,
                    In the cauldron boil aid bake;
                    Eye of newt and toe of frog,
                    Wool of bat and tongue of dog,
                    Adder's fork and blind worm's sting,
                    Lizard's leg and howler's wing,
                    For a charm of powerful trouble,
                    Like a hell-broth boil and bubble.

All.   Double, double toil and trouble;
                    Fire burn and cauldron bubble.

Third Witch.   Scale of dragon, tooth of wolf,
                    Witches' mummy, maw and gulf
                    Of the ravin'd salt-sea shark,
                    Root of hemlock digg'd i' the dark,

	Add thereto a tiger's chaudron,
	For the ingredients of our cauldron.
All.	Double, double toil and trouble;
	Fire burn and cauldron bubble.
Second Witch.	Cool it with a baboon's blood,
	Then the charm is firm and good.
	(Enter Hecate.)
Hecate.	O, well done! I commend your pains;
	And everyone shall share i' the gains:
	And now about the cauldron sing,
	Like elves and fairies in a ring,
	Enchanting all that you put in.

—WILLIAM SHAKESPEARE

The Witchcraft Trial of Kit Tyler

When Kit Tyler was sixteen, her Grandfather died and she was left alone with no home, no money, trunks full of beautiful clothes which she was accustomed to wearing, and boat fare from Barbados to Wethersfield, Connecticut. An aunt and uncle whom she never had seen lived there, and she hoped they would welcome her into their home. Otherwise, what else could she do? Where could she go?

On the long voyage by sailing ship from her Barbados childhood home, Kit thought often of Grandfather. He had been a wonderful companion, sailing and swimming with her, and teaching her to read and write very well and to enjoy many, many good books. She did not realize, in this year of 1687, how unusual it was for a girl to be so well educated, and, also, to be able to swim. In many places in New England and elsewhere girls did not swim, because it was thought that only witches could float in water without drowning. But all of these things Kit was to find out later, to her sorrow. Grandfather had taught her to be brave, too; and even though all the luxuries with which she had grown up were swept away after his death, and she was so very alone, she met her new life bravely.

She certainly needed courage with someone like Goodwife Cruff around, for from the minute that woman had boarded the ship with her solemn husband and frightened little girl, Kit could feel her dislike. Goodwife Cruff stared scornfully at Kit's scarlet cloak and elegant silk dress, then rudely pushed her husband and little Prudence past Kit. Timid little Prudence carried a wooden dolly, most lovingly. Halfway across the harbor, the ship tossed and the little girl was flung to the edge. Her mother jerked her back, cuffing her hard, and the doll was knocked overboard and bobbed helplessly in the water.

Prudence wailed "My dolly's gone!" but her mother shouted, "Shame on you!" and smacked her again. The Captain, busy with the boat, paid no attention to Prudence' sorrow nor the lost doll. Kit threw off her shoes and cloak, dived in, and swam for the doll. The Captain's son, Nat, thinking Kit could not swim, dived in to save her life. When she swam back triumphantly with the doll, Kit was alarmed by the horror and anger on all the passengers' faces. Later when they avoided her, and Goodwife Cruff pulled Prudence away from sitting near her at meals, Kit was shocked to learn they thought her a witch.

Life in Wethersfield was not easy for Kit, for even her Aunt Rachel and Uncle Matthew Wood found her hard to understand. She had been brought up so differently from their children and from their neighbors' children; and she was very impulsive. Goodwife Cruff spread malicious rumors about Kit constantly. On the other hand, little Prudence Cruff adored Kit; and even though the child's mother had persuaded her father that Prudence was very stupid and could not be taught, Kit secretly taught her to read very well, with the help of a horn book and a copy book.

Through constantly spying, Goodwife Cruff found that Kit went often to the little house of Widow Hannah Tupper whom most people shunned, calling her the Witch of Blackbird Pond. At last, Goodwife Cruff openly accused Kit of being a witch, had her arrested and brought to trial. Frightened and bewildered, at the trial Kit heard different people blame all sorts of misfortunes on her because she was a witch.

Captain Talcott, the Magistrate, presided over a group of selectmen who formed the court. Uncle Matthew was one of them and Kit could see that he was sad for her. Mr. Woodbridge and Dr. Bulkeley, famous *for their sermons against witchcraft, were present, also, listening to all the accusations against Kit and shaking their heads. Kit did not know how to defend herself against the lies being told about her.*

The rest of the story of Kit's trial follows, as it is told in the suspenseful book The Witch of Blackbird Pond *by Elizabeth George Speare. This book, published by Houghton Mifflin Company, won a Newbery Award.*

The Witchcraft Trial of Kit Tyler

Matthew Wood leaped suddenly to his feet. "I protest this mockery!" he roared in a voice that silenced every whisper. "Not one word of this nonsense could be proved in the Court of Assistants. There is not one shred of lawful evidence in the lot! I beg you, Sam Talcott, make an end of it!"

"Do I infer that you are willing to vouch for your niece's good character, Matthew Wood?"

"Certainly. I will vouch for it."

"We are to understand then that these visits to the Widow Tupper were taken with your approval?"

Taken aback, Matthew glared at the magistrate. "No, I had no knowledge of them," he admitted.

"Did you ever, at any time, indicate to your niece that she was not to associate with this woman?"

"Yes, I forbade her to go."

"Then the girl has been disobedient and deceitful."

Matthew clenched his fist in frustration. "The girl has been thoughtless and headstrong at times. But her upbringing has been such as to encourage that."

"You admit then that her education has been irregular?"

"You can twist what I say as you will, Sam Talcott," said Matthew in steely anger. "But I swear before all present, on my word as a freeman of the colony, that the girl is no witch."

"We are obliged to listen to the testimony, Matthew," said Captain Talcott reasonably. "I will thank you to keep silent. What is your opinion of the case, Dr. Bulkeley?"

Dr. Bulkeley cleared his throat. "In my opinion," he said deliberately, "it is necessary to use the greatest caution in the matter of testimony. Since the unnatural events so far recounted appear to rest in each case upon the word of but one witness, the legality of any one of them is open to question."

"It is ridiculous to talk of legality," interrupted Matthew. "There has not one word been spoken that makes sense!"

For the last few moments Goodwife Cruff had been vehemently prodding her husband. He rose now obediently. "Sir, I've summat to say as makes sense," he announced, assuming a bold tone, "and there's more than one witness to prove it. I've got summat here as was found in the widow's house that night."

With a sinking heart Kit watched as he drew an object from his pocket. It was not the hornbook, as she expected. It was the little copybook. At sight of it Goodwife Cruff's anger burst through all restraints.

"Look at that!" she demanded. "What do you say about that? My Prudence's name, written over and over. 'Tis a spell, that's what it is! A mercy the child is alive today. Another hour and she'd have been dying like the others!"

The magistrate accepted the copybook reluctantly, as though it were tainted.

"Do you recognize this book, Mistress Tyler?"

Kit could barely stand upright. She tried to answer, but only a hoarse whisper came out.

"Speak up, girl!" he ordered sharply. "Does this book belong to you?"

"Yes, sir," she managed.

"Did you write this name?"

Kit could barely swallow. She had vowed she would never deceive her uncle again! Then, remembering, she looked back at the copybook. Yes, the name on the first line was in her own hand, large and clear for Prudence to copy. "Yes, sir," she said, her voice loud with relief. "I wrote the name."

Matthew Wood passed a hand over his eyes. He looked old, old and ill.

"Why should you write a child's name over and over like that?"

"I—I can't tell you sir."

Captain Talcott looked perplexed. "There are no other children's names here," he said. "Why did you choose to write the name of Prudence Cruff?"

Kit was silent.

"Mistress Tyler." The magistrate spoke to her directly. "I had considered this morning's inquiry merely a formality. I did not expect to find any evidence worthy of carrying to the court. But this is a serious matter. You must explain to us how this child's name came to be written."

As Kit looked back at him mutely, the restraints that held the tensely waiting crowd gave way. Men and women leaped to their feet, screaming.

"She won't answer! That proves she's guilty!"

"She's a witch! She's as good as admitted it!"

"We don't need a jury trial. Put her to the water test!"

"Hanging's too good for her!"

In the midst of the pandemonium Gershom Bulkeley quietly reached for the copybook, studied it carefully, and turned a shrewd, deliberate eye upon Kit. Then he whispered something to the magistrate. Captain Talcott nodded.

"Silence!" he barked. "This is the Colony of Connecticut! Every man and woman is entitled to a trial before a jury. This case will be turned over to the General Session in Hartford. The inquiry is dismissed."

"Hold a minute, Captain!" called a voice. A commotion near the door had been scarcely noticed. "There's a fellow here says he has an important witness for the case."

Every voice was suddenly stilled. Almost paralyzed with dread, Kit turned slowly to face a new accuser. On the threshold of the room stood Nat Eaton, slim, straight-shouldered, without a trace of mockery in his level blue eyes.

Nat! The wave of joy and relief was so unexpected that she almost lost her balance, but almost instantly it was drained away and left a new fear. For she saw that beside him, clinging tightly to his hand, was Prudence Cruff.

Goodwife Cruff let out a piercing scream. "Take her out of here! The witch will put an evil eye on her!" She and her husband both started forward.

"Stand back!" ordered the magistrate. "The child is protected here. Where is the witness?"

Nat put his hands on the child's shoulders and gently urged her forward. With one trusting look up at his face, Prudence walked steadily toward the magistrate's table.

Suddenly Kit found her voice. "Oh, please sir!" she cried, the tears rushing down her face, "Let them take her away! It is all my fault! I would do anything to undo it if I could! I never meant any harm, but I'm responsible for all of it. Please—take me to Hartford. Do what you want with me. But—oh, I beg you—send Prudence away from this horrible place!"

The magistrate waited till this outburst was over. " 'Tis a trifle late to think about the child," he said coldly. "Come here, child."

Kit sank on her knees and buried her face in her hands. The buzz in the room roared like a swarm of bees around her head. Then there was a waiting hush. She could scarcely bear to look at Prudence, but she forced herself to raise her head. The child was barefoot and her snarled hair was uncovered. Her thin arms, under the skimpy jumper, were blue with cold. Then Kit stared again. There was something strange about Prudence.

"Will you stand there, child, in front of the table?" Captain Talcott spoke reassuringly.

Watching Prudence, Kit suddenly felt a queer prickling along her spine. There *was* something different about her. The child's head was up. Her eyes were fastened levelly on the magistrate. Prudence was not afraid!

"We will ask you some questions, Prudence," said the magistrate quietly. "You will answer them as truthfully as you possibly can. Do you understand?"

"Yes, sir," whispered Prudence.

"Do you know this young woman?"

"Oh, yes, sir. She is my teacher. She taught me to read."

"You mean at the dame school?"

"No, I never went to the dame school."

"Then where did she teach you?"

"At Hannah's house in the meadow."

A loud scream from Goodwife Cruff tore across the room.

"You mean Mistress Tyler took you to Hannah Tupper's house?"

"The first time she took me there. After that I went by myself."

"The little weasel!" cried Goodwife Cruff. "That's where she was all those days. I'll see that girl hung!"

It is all over, thought Kit, with a wave of faintness. Gershom Bulkeley still held the little copybook. He spoke now, under his breath, and passed the book to Captain Talcott.

"Have you seen this book before?" the magistrate questioned.

"Oh, yes, sir. Kit gave it to me. I wrote my name in it."

"That's a lie!" cried Goodwife Cruff. "The child is bewitched!"

Captain Talcott turned to Kit. "Is it true," he asked her, "that the child wrote her own name in this book?"

Kit dragged herself to her feet. "'Tis true," she answered dully. "I wrote it for her once and then she copied it."

"You can't take her word for anything, sir," protested Goodman Cruff timidly. "The child don't know what she's saying. I might as well tell it, Prudence has never been what you'd call bright. She never could learn much."

The magistrate paid no attention. "Could you write your name again, do you think?"

"I—I think so, sir."

He dipped the quill pen carefully in the ink and handed it to the child. Leaning over the table, Prudence set the pen on the copybook. For a moment there was not a single sound in the room but the hesitant scratching.

Goodman Cruff was on his feet. Propelled by a curiosity greater than any awe for the magistrate, he came slowly across the room and peered over his child's shoulder.

"Is that proper writing?" he demanded in unbelief. "Prudence Cruff, does it say, right out as it should?"

The magistrate glanced at the writing and handed the copybook to Gershom Bulkeley.

"Very proper writing, I should say," Dr. Bulkeley commented, "For a child with no learning."

The magistrate leaned to take the pen out of the small fingers. Goodman Cruff tiptoed back to the bench. The bluster was gone from him. He looked dazed.

"Now Prudence," the magistrate continued. "You say that Mistress Tyler taught you to read?"

"What sort of reading?" Goodwife Cruff rose in a frenzy. "Magic signs and spells I tell you! The child would never know the difference."

Gershom Bulkeley also rose to his feet. "That at least will be easy to prove," he suggested reasonably. "What can you read, child?"

"I can read the Bible."

Dr. Bulkeley picked up the Great Bible from the table and turned the pages thoughtfully. Then, moving to hand the Book to Prudence, he realized that it was too heavy for her to hold and laid it carefully on the table beside her. "Read that for us, child, beginning right there."

Kit held her breath. Was it the tick of the great clock that sounded so frightening, or her own heart? Then across the silence came a whisper.

> "Buy the truth, and sell it not;
> also wis-wisdom, and in-in-instruction, and
> understanding."

The childish voice slowly gained strength and clarity till it reached to every corner of the room.

"The father of the right-righteous shall greatly
rejoice; and he that begetteth a wise child shall
have joy of him. Thy father and thy mother shall be
glad, and she that bare thee shall rejoice."

In the warm rush of pride that welled up in her, Kit forgot her fear. For the first time she dared to look back at Nat Eaton where he stood near the door. Across the room their eyes met, and suddenly it was as though he had thrown a line straight into her reaching hands. She could feel the pull of it, and over its taut span strength flowed into her, warm and sustaining.

When finally she looked away she realized that everyone in the room was staring at the two parents. They had both leaned forward, their mouths open in shock and unbelief. As she listened, Goodwife Cruff's face darkened and her eyes narrowed. She saw now that she had been tricked. The fresh anger that was gathering would be vented on her child.

On the father's face a new emotion seemed to be struggling. As the thin voice ended, Goodwife Cruff drew in her breath through her teeth in a venomous hiss. But before she could release it her husband sprang forward.

"Did you hear that?" he demanded widely, of everyone present. All at once his shoulders straightened. "That was real good reading. I'd like to see any boy in this town do better!"

"It's a trick!" denied his wife. "That child could never read a word in her life! She's bewitched, I tell you!"

"Hold your tongue, woman," shouted her husband unexpectedly. "I'm sick and tired of hearing about Prudence being bewitched. All these years you been telling me our child was half-witted. Why, she's smart as a whip. I bet it warn't much of a trick to teach her to read."

Goodwife Cruff's jaw dropped. For one moment she was struck utterly dumb, and in that moment her husband stepped into his rightful place. There was a new authority in his voice.

"All my life I've wished I could read. If I'd had a son, I'd of seen to it he learned his letters. Well, this is a new country over here, and who says it may not be just as needful for a woman to read as a man? Might give her summat to think about besides witches and foolishness. Any rate, I got someone now to read the Good Book to me of an evening, and if that's the work of the devil, then I say 'tis a mighty queer thing for the devil to go working against himself!"

The magistrate had not interrupted this speech. There was a glint of amusement in his eye as he asked, "I take it then, Goodman Cruff, that you withdraw your charges against this young woman?"

"Yes," he answered loudly. "Yes. I'll withdraw the charges."

"Adam Cruff?" His wife had found her voice. "Have ye lost your senses? The girl has bewitched you too!"

In the back of the room someone tittered. A man's laugh rang out—was it Nat's? All at once, like a clap of thunder, the tension of the room broke into laughter that shook the timbers and rattled the windows. Every man in the room was secretly applauding Adam Cruff's declaration of independence. Even the magistrate's stern lips twisted slightly.

"There seems to be no evidence of witchcraft," he announced, when order had been restored. "The girl has admitted her wrong in encouraging a child to willful disobedience. Beyond that I cannot see that there is any reasonable charge against her. I pronounce that Mistress Katherine Tyler is free and innocent."

—ELIZABETH GEORGE SPEARE

Witches' Fete

Now to the Brocken the witches hie,
The stubble is yellow, the corn is green;
Thither the gathering legions fly,
And sitting aloft is Sir U'-ri-an seen;
O'er stick and o'er stone they go whirling along,
Witches and he-goats, a motley throng.
Alone old Baubo's coming now;
She rides upon a farrow sow,
A goodly sow and mother thereon,
The whole witch chorus follows anon.

The way is broad, the way is long.
What mad pursuit, what tumult wide!
The wind is hushed, the stars grow pale,
The pensive moon her light doth veil,
And whirling on, the magic choir
Sputter forth sparks of drizzling fire.

.   .   .   .

Broom and pitchfork, goat and prong,
Mounted on these we whirl along.
Who vainly strives to climb tonight
Is evermore a luckless wight.

—JOHANN WOLFGANG VON GOETHE

Parson Walker Preaches on Witchcraft

Elijah Fletcher's congregation
Aroused his worry and vexation.
He preached to them of Heavenly Riches,
But busybodies buzzed of witches.
Elijah asked the Concord parson
To come and douse this vocal arson.
Timothy preached, when he had prayed,
Spoke quietly, "Be not afraid.
To banish witches we must never
Discuss the creatures, but forever
Ignore, erase and blot then out."
And that is how it came about,
On sulky broomsticks, one by one,
All witches fled from Hopkinton.

—ELEANOR VINTON

Note: The Reverend Elijah Fletcher was pastor of the Hopkinton Congregational Church from 1773 to 1786, the year of his death. The Reverend Timothy Walker was pastor of the First Congregational Church of Concord from 1730 till his death in 1782. (From *Boston's History of Concord and History of Merrimack & Belknap Counties,* edited by D. Hamilton Hurd.)

Ghost Stories and Legends

People all over the world, for thousands of years, have wondered and talked about the mystery of death and of what happens to the spirits of the dead. Worship of ancestors was once an important part of religion, and it was thought that the spirits of these ancestors often returned to visit the family. If a relative had been treated badly when he was alive, his spirit or ghost might pay off the grudge some dark night. Or other ghosts might haunt a place, ready to harm those who had been unfair.

Sometimes ghosts came back to try to make up for some wrong they had done. Since ghosts often knew where treasure had been hidden, they might return to lead a person to the buried treasure.

Usually ghosts have been thought to wander in the dark or gloomy semi-darkness, and to disappear with the first light of dawn. This idea may have started long ago when people worshiped the sun. The sun helped crops grow, gave light and a safe feeling, whereas darkness was a mysterious symbol of evil, danger, and death.

Naturally, when there are great mysteries all sorts of stories and legends are told concerning them. Perhaps ghost stories were told first in caves, later in lonely villages, in castles, in cities, and now in books, and on radio and television. Long before people could read or be entertained by radio or television, they often gathered for a little excitement around the fire on a chilly evening and told ghost stories. Some told tales they had heard from their grandparents; some told of their own daring experiences with ghosts.

Then, prickly with fright, children would scurry to bed; and neighbors would huddle together as they went out into the spooky darkness to return home. They jumped in fright at every twig that snapped, every owl that hooted. Some shrieked and ran when the bare branches of a dark tree creaked and swayed with the eerie night wind in the pale moonlight. From such incidents they might have more tales to tell of meeting ghosts or specters on the road.

And woe to anyone who had to pass an old empty house after dark! Old houses were said to be favorite places of ghosts.

Ghosts were thought to drift over graveyards, especially in mist and fog, and sometimes they danced there. In passing a graveyard a person might hold his breath and tiptoe by. If a live person's spirit escaped with his breath it might be captured by ghosts. This superstition came from a very ancient belief that a person's spirit, or life force, was in his breath, and that enemies or evil spirits lurked near to snatch it. Many eerie stories are set in graveyards.

Every nation has its ghost stories. Many are much alike, even though most ghost stories originally were told about frightening happenings in the home or neighborhood. Some stories have ghostly horses and riders, hunters, hounds, horns, bells, and so forth. Sometimes goblins, witches, wizards, or the devil appear in ghost stories, as in all sorts of spooky tales.

Mysterious lights are told about in ghost stories of many lands. In the western North Carolina hills not far from Morganton, the Brown Mountain Lights have mystified thousands of people who have come to see them from many states and countries.

"Sometimes the lights can be seen and sometimes they can't. But usually, in fair weather, not too much patience is required for a look at the bobbing lights. Persons who wish to see the lights can take their position at Wiseman's View on Highway No. 105 near Morganton about eight o'clock in the evening and look to the southeast. The Linville-Grandfather Mountain area is also another vantage. Suddenly there will appear a light about the size of a toy balloon. It is very red in color, will rise over the summit of the mountain, hover there momentarily, then disappear.

"In a few minutes the light will appear at another point on the mountain. And so, through the night, the lights appear, disappear, reappear at different points around that mountain, but nowhere else."

People often do not agree on what they see. One says the light is almost white and appears in a definite circle, while another a few miles away says the light is a glowing, yellowish ball of fire which appears later like an extremely bright bursting skyrocket. Although scientific studies have been made of these lights, and through the years thousands of people have watched them, they still remain a mountain mystery.

Naturally, many spooky tales have been told and retold about the mysterious Brown Mountain Lights. One story began in 1850 after a woman in that region disappeared. Her husband was suspected of murdering her. Search groups looked all over the mountainside for her body. Then, suddenly one dark night strange lights appeared over Brown Mountain. Nobody ever had seen such lights there before.

"Some were scared and contended that the lights, bobbing away there, were the spirit of the dead woman come back to haunt her murderer—and maybe keep people from searching for her body."

No trace of the body was found. But "a little while after that, a man who was a relative newcomer left with a fine horse and wagon that had belonged to the missing woman's husband. The husband said the man had bought them, but everyone knew the newcomer had shown no evidence of having money. He was never heard from again, but people assumed he had either helped with the murder or had known of it and been bribed to leave."

This story has been told from person to person for more than a hundred years and is included in the book, *The Devil's Tramping Ground and Other North Carolina Stories,* by John Harden, published by the University of North Carolina Press, Chapel Hill, 1949. This book retells, also, some famous legends of ghost ships.

One such ghost ship mystery comes from the Hatteras section of the Outer Banks of North Carolina, known often as "the graveyard of ships." Here on Diamond Shoals early one morning in February, 1921, was sighted a five-masted schooner under full sail, heaving mightily, with her prow cut deep in the sand.

"The morning watch at the near-by Cape Hatteras Coast Guard station was momentarily stunned by the eerie spectacle. There had been no storm. The last watch to scan the shore and sea before darkness closed in the night before had reported all clear and calm, with neither sail nor smoke in sight. No light had been shown during the night, and no distress signals had been sent up.

"What ship was this? Where did she come from? How could she possibly have grounded? Why had not the crew given some sign of the ship's distress?"

When the Coast Guardsmen were able to battle their way through pounding seas amid the dread shoals the only living thing found on the ship was a lean gray cat! What had become of the crew?

The ship was the *Carroll M. Deering* from Bath, Maine. Six government departments besides the Coast Guard searched and searched for clues to the mystery of the wreck and the disappearance of the crew. No clues ever could be found!

Several weeks after the ship first was seen foundering in the waves, the stern broke away and landed on a beach about twelve miles away. Hundreds of gulls came to roost on it. Their shrill, eerie cries made the nights hideous. Natives on the nearby beach heard talk of spirits walking on the ghost ship and finally asked the government to destroy it. Even after the ship was blown up, many people still were frightened because hundreds and hundreds of gulls circled and recircled the spot, screeching and crying. Tales were told that these noises were the cries of departed spirits hovering near the scattered remains of the ghost ship.

Another ghost ship legend from North Carolina tells of a ship that floated into port in 1812 with no life aboard. This was scary enough! But there was a mysterious portrait found on the ship. For many years afterward this picture hung on the wall of a shack near the beach where the ghostly ship first had been sighted. Then the portrait was identified as that of Theodosia Burr, Aaron Burr's daughter. Nobody ever could find out how it came to be on the ship, or what happened to the beautiful Theodosia, who was believed to have been a passenger. At times some people think they see the lovely girl's ghost in mists drifting in from the sea.

Many seacoasts have their own ghost ship tales. *The Flying Dutchman (Der Fliegende Hollander)*, an opera by Richard Wagner, is taken from a medieval legend of a Dutch navigator condemned endlessly to roam the seas in his sailing ship. Once every seven years the ghostly seafarer could go ashore to see his wife.

Maine, with hundreds of miles of seacoast, has many ghost ship legends. In one, the ghost ship of Harpswell will appear suddenly, and sail near shore, but it never can be lured to land. Often it is an omen of death to someone who sees it. Among the many spooky tales of Prince Edward Island is one of a phantom ship that appeared in 1786 near Sea Cow Head Lighthouse and was seen many times afterward, but always disappeared when pursued. Some people think it was one of Captain Kidd's pirate ships.

Stories of pirates' ghost ships still are told, and Captain Kidd, Bluebeard, and others terrify people in ghostly ways. Some tales are about phantom ships that return to haunt and trouble the conscience of murderous sea-robbers. In these tales the murdered passengers, officers, and crew return to the ship they were sailing when it was boarded by the pirates. The ghosts themselves may not be seen, but the ghost ship that had been sunk by the pirates appears by the light of a pale moon on the anniversary of the crime. Then it vanishes, leaving the robbers sleepless and almost frantic. So it is in many tales, the ghost of the victim of past bad deeds returns to haunt the one who did wrong.

Some folk say that the ghost ship on the Hudson River is manned by Henry Hudson who sailed up the river more than 350 years ago looking for the passage to India. Others say the ship carries ghosts of his crew who mutinied and set him adrift in a small boat. Still others think it is an unknown ship that might have been condemned by the Storm King never to reach shore because the skipper had not shown him proper respect. This Storm King was a terrible goblin who lived on Dunderberg, or Thunder Mountain, overlooking the river at a treacherous place. Most Dutch skippers on the Hudson respectfully dipped their sails to him when they neared that place.

Many other river valleys throughout the world have tales of phantom ships, river ghosts, goblins, and sprites. Also, spooks haunt places like Sleepy Hollow in New York and Sleepy Hollow on Prince Edward Isle, and are at work on various spook hills.

Sometimes a ghost will return or give a signal to warn his family or neighborhood or country of danger and urge them to meet the danger bravely. One legend tells that when England is in danger "Drake's drum" is heard, and Admiral Francis Drake, who saved England 400 years ago by defeating the Spanish Armada, is drumming up the people to new courage. Sometimes, it is said, Admiral Nelson's signal rallies the British to a courageous stand.

Some famous ghosts are Marley's ghost in Dicken's *Christmas Carol,* and Banquo's ghost in Shakespeare's *Macbeth.* They are among the many ghosts who haunt persons who have been ruthless and greedy for money or power.

Since many ghost stories are connected with the search for gold, old mine sites often have ghosts. Many spooky tales are told about violent deaths and mysterious disappearances of persons searching for gold at the Lost Dutchman Mine of Superstition Mountain in Arizona.

In Mexico, sometimes, the kind ghost of an old prospector who had stored a secret horde of gold will appear and try to lead some poor, honest, hard-working man to that gold. Although transparent, the ghost is recognized by the blue light he carries.

So it is that all around the world accounts of ghosts may be scary, spooky tales or stories of helpful, kind ghosts. And, as years go by, many more stories about ghosts will be told as people have mysterious experiences that remind them of persons who once have lived. Many such experiences are hard to explain, and, naturally, when retold again and again the story is added to and often changed.

People everywhere often recall with happy memories the good spirit of some family member or friend, and tell pleasant stories about that person and are thankful for the many good ways in which he helped the family. From ancient times some people in various parts of the world have felt that such kindly spirits of ancestors are nearby, guarding them and their homes from evil and bringing them happiness. So they hold festivals to honor the dead.

Mexico has one such famous festival of happy remembrance of the dead; and in Taipei, Formosa, a Ghost Festival is held each year, when sacrifices are offered to ancestors and to wandering ghosts who have no descendants to honor them. Travelers from a number of countries visit Formosa at the time of the festival, which in 1970 was August 16. They not only share in remembering the ancestors of Formosan people, but they return to their own countries, recalling stories of their own ancestors.

The great mystery of life and death and the human spirit fascinates people all over the world.

—MILDRED CORELL LUCKHARDT

The Legend of Sleepy Hollow
(or *The Headless Horseman*)

On the shore of a spacious cove of the Hudson River, called the Tappan Zee by ancient Dutch navigators, there was a small market town known as Tarry Town. Not far from this village, perhaps three miles, was a little valley among high hills, called Sleepy Hollow. Many of the early Dutch settlers declared this quiet valley to be bewitched; and the whole neighborhood was filled with tales of haunted spots and twilight superstitions.

The ghostly spirit that seemed to command all others who haunted this region was the apparition seen by the country folk, of a figure on horseback without a head, hurrying along in the gloom of night as if on the wings of the wind. Sometimes he haunted nearby roads, especially in the vicinity of a church not far off.

To this lonely Sleepy Hollow came Ichabod Crane to be the schoolteacher, or pedagogue. He was tall but exceedingly thin, with narrow shoulders, long arms and legs, hand that dangled a mile out of his sleeves, feet that might have served for shovels, and his whole frame most loosely hung together. To see him striding along the profile of a hill on a windy day one might have mistaken him for a scarecrow escaped from some cornfield.

Besides being schoolteacher he was the singing-master of the neighborhood singing school; and he thought himself a very fine singer. Since the schoolmaster was considered important by the young girls and women of a neighborhood, he often was invited out for a meal. After eating, he would tell many fearful ghost stories. And on long winter evenings he would crowd close to the fire with old Dutch wives and listen to their marvelous tales of ghosts, goblins, haunted fields, haunted brooks, haunted bridges, and haunted houses. A favorite tale was about the Headless Horseman of Sleepy Hollow. Then, later, as Ichabod walked homeward, what fearful shapes and shadows beset his path amidst the dim and ghastly glare of a snowy night!

Among the young people who came to Ichabod's music school was Katrina Van Tassel, the only child of a substantial Dutch farmer who was wealthy and liberal-hearted. Katrina was a blooming lass of eighteen, rosy-cheeked as one of her father's peaches and famed for her beauty. She was also a little of a coquette. Ichabod Crane had a soft and foolish heart toward the ladies, and it was not to be wondered that so tempting a morsel soon found favor in his eyes, especially after he had visited in her father's very comfortable mansion.

As he went through the flourishing Van Tassel fields and saw the huge barns already filling with food for the winter, and all the farm animals, Ichabod's mouth began to water. He pictured every roasting pig already with an apple in its mouth, the geese swimming in their own gravy, and the ducks tastily roasted and covered with onion sauce. His busy fancy already had him wed to the blooming Katrina.

He immediately set out to court the young lady, but he ran into many difficulties. He had to win his way into the heart of a coquette who had many admirers, all of whom were besieging her and keeping a watchful, angry eye on one another, yet all were ready to band together against any newcomer. The most formidable rival was a burly, roaring, roystering blade nicknamed Brom Bones because of his huge frame and great strength. He was a famed horseman, dashing about with several boon companions to every scene of feud or merriment for miles around.

When Brom Bones's horse was seen tied to the Van Tassel paling on a Sunday night, all other suitors passed in despair and gave way to Brom. Ichabod, however, did not give up. Being afraid to cross Brom openly, he courted Katrina in many quiet, chivalrous ways, and Brom Bones's horse no longer was tied to the Van Tassel palings on Sunday nights. A feud arose between Brom and the pedagogue of Sleepy Hollow.

Brom Bones would have liked to settle the matter openly with a fist fight or wrestling match, but Ichabod carefully avoided this. So Bones and his gang of rough riders began to play practical jokes on his rival. They stuffed the chimney and smoked out the singing-school, and Brom even taught his dog to whine in a ludicrous manner as a rival of Ichabod's singing.

Matters went on in this way for some time without any real results with the fair Katrina. Then, one autumn afternoon, one of the Van Tassel servants rode to the schoolhouse door with an invitation to Ichabod to attend a quilting frolic and harvest supper that evening.

Ichabod dismissed school hastily and spent a long time brushing his hair and getting himself ready. He borrowed a horse from Hans Van Ripper, the choleric farmer at whose home he lived, and rode off like a knight-errant. The animal was a broken-down plow horse that had outlived almost everything but his viciousness. He was gaunt and shagged; his rusty mane and tail were tangled with burrs; one eye had lost its pupil, but the other had the gleam of a devil in it. Still he must have had fire in his day for he was named Gunpowder. Ichabod rode with short stirrups, his knees nearly up to the pommel of the saddle; his sharp elbows stuck out like grasshoppers' knees; the motion of his arms was not unlike the flapping of wings.

It was toward evening that Ichabod arrived at the castle of Heer Van Tassel, which was decorated with masses of flowers of the adjacent countryside. Brom Bones, however, was the hero of the scene, having come on his favorite horse Daredevil, a creature that no one but Brom could manage.

Ichabod did not let Brom's presence destroy his enjoyment of the feast—the heaped up platters of chicken and ham and smoked beef, to say nothing of the apple pies, peach pies, and pumpkin pies. No one could count all the delicious kinds of cakes and doughnuts, olykoeks, crullers, and the various preserved fruits. Ichabod took his time and did ample justice to every dainty. His spirits rose with eating, and he could not help rolling his eyes round him as he ate and chuckling with the possibility that he might one day be lord of all this scene. On that day he'd turn his back upon the old schoolhouse, and snap his fingers in the face of Hans Van Ripper.

After awhile the sound of music summoned them to the dance. Ichabod prided himself upon his dancing. Not a limb, not a fiber about him was idle. The lady of his heart was his graciously smiling partner in the dance. Brom Bones, sorely smitten with love and jealousy, sat brooding in one corner.

When the dance was at an end, Ichabod was attracted to a knot of folks who sat with old Van Tassel smoking on the piazza, drawing out long stories about the war. But these were nothing to the tales of ghosts and apparitions that followed. The chief part of the stories turned upon the specter, the headless horseman of Sleepy Hollow, who had been seen several times of late and who tethered his horse nightly among the graves in the churchyard.

Tale after tale was told of this ghostly horseman. Brom Bones made light of this specter, saying that one midnight when the galloping ghost overtook him he raced with him for a bowl of punch and Daredevil beat the goblin horse, but just as they came to the church bridge the horse and rider vanished in the flash of fire.

The revel now gradually broke up. The farmers gathered their families in the wagons and were heard for some time rattling along the hollow roads and over the dark distant hills, the sounds becoming fainter until they died away. Ichabod alone lingered behind to have a talk with the heiress. Nobody knows what was said, but soon he sallied forth, quite desolate and crestfallen. He went straight to the stable and roused his horse rudely with several kicks.

It was the very witching time of night that Ichabod, heavyhearted, traveled homeward along the sides of the hills that rise above Tarry Town. All the stories of ghosts and goblins that he had heard came crowding upon his memory. The night grew darker and darker. He never had felt so lonely and dismal. He was approaching the place where many scenes of the ghost stories had been laid. In the center of the road towered an enormous tulip tree like a giant. The common people regarded it with respect and superstition, for many tales of strange sights and lamentations were told about it.

With fear and misgivings, Ichabod at last passed the tree, but new perils lay before him. About two hundred yards from the tree, a small brook crossed the road and ran into a marshy, thickly wooded glen. A few rough logs served as a bridge over this stream. On that side of the road where the brook entered the wood, oaks and chestnut trees, matted thick with wild grapevines, threw a cavernous gloom over it. This bridge was the severest trial. This had ever been considered a haunted stream, fearful to pass alone after dark.

As Ichabod approached the stream his heart thumped; he gave his horse a kick in the ribs and attempted to dash across the bridge. But instead of starting forward the perverse animal ran broadside against the fence. Ichabod jerked the reins on the other side and kicked with the other foot. All in vain! His steed plunged to the opposite side of the road into a thicket of brambles and alder bushes. The schoolmaster kicked and whipped Gunpowder, who dashed forward snorting, but stopped by the bridge so suddenly that Ichabod nearly went sprawling over his head.

At that moment a splashy sound by the side of the bridge caught Ichabod's ear. In the dark shadow of the grove on the margin of the brook he beheld something huge, misshapen, eerie, towering. It stirred not, but seemed gathered up in the gloom like some gigantic monster ready to spring upon the traveler.

What was to be done? To turn and fly was now too late. Besides what chance was there of escaping ghost or goblin which could ride upon the wings of the wind? Summoning a show of courage, he stammered, "Who are you?" No reply. He repeated his demand in a still more frightened voice. Still no answer. Once more he beat Gunpowder's sides and, shutting his eyes, broke forth into a psalm tune. The frightful shadowy object, with a scramble and bound, stood in the middle of the road.

Though the night was dark, the object seemed to be a very large horseman mounted on a powerful black horse. He made no sign but kept on one side of the road, jogging along on the blind side of Gunpowder, who had now got over his fright.

Ichabod, who had no relish for this strange midnight companion and could think only of the adventure of Brom Bones with the headless horseman, now quickened his steed in hopes of leaving the intruder behind. The stranger quickened his horse to an equal pace. Ichabod pulled up and fell into a walk, thinking to lag behind. The other did the same. His heart began to sink within him. He tried to resume his psalm tune but his parched tongue clove to the roof of his mouth and he could not utter a sound.

There was something mysterious and appalling about the silence of this companion. It was soon fearfully accounted for. On mounting a rising ground which brought the figure of his fellow-traveler in relief against the sky, gigantic and muffled in a cloak, Ichabod was horror-struck to see that he was headless! His horror was increased on observing that the head, which should have rested on the silent rider's shoulders, was carried before him on the pommel of his saddle.

Terrified and desperate, Ichabod rained kicks and blows upon Gunpowder, hoping by a sudden movement to give his companion the slip—but the specter started full jump with him. Away they dashed through thick and thin, stones flying, sparks flashing at every bound. Ichabod's flimsy garments fluttered in the air as he stretched his long lank body over his horse's head in the eagerness of flight.

They had now reached the road which turns off to Sleepy Hollow, but Gunpowder, who seemed possessed with a demon, made an

opposite turn and plunged headlong downhill to the left. This road leads through a sandy hollow, shaded by trees for about a quarter of a mile, where it crosses the bridge famous in goblin story. Just beyond swells the green knoll on which stands the whitewashed church.

So far the panic of Ichabod's steed had given him apparent advantage in the chase. But as he got halfway through the hollow the girths of the saddle gave way, and he felt it slipping from under him. He seized it by the pommel and endeavoured to hold it firm, but in vain. He had just time to save himself by clasping old Gunpowder round the neck when the saddle fell to the earth and he heard it trampled under foot by his pursuer. The goblin was hard on his haunches. Unskilled rider that Ichabod was, he had much ado to maintain his seat, sometimes slipping on one side, sometimes on another, sometimes jolted on the high ridge of the horse's backbone with a violence he feared would cleave him in two.

An opening in the trees now cheered him with hope that the church bridge was at hand. The wavering reflection of a silver star in the brook told him he was not mistaken. He saw the church walls grimly glaring under the trees beyond, and remembered the place where Brom Bones's ghostly competitor had disappeared. Ichabod thought, "If I can reach that bridge, I am safe."

Just then he heard the black steed panting and blowing close behind him. Another kick in the ribs and Gunpowder sprang upon the bridge; he thundered over the planks; he gained the opposite side. Now Ichabod looked behind to see if his pursuer should vanish according to rule in a flash of fire and brimstone. Just then he saw the goblin rising in the stirrups, in the very act of hurling his head at him. Ichabod tried to dodge the horrible missile. Too late! It hit his head with a tremendous crash. He was tumbled headlong into

the dust; and Gunpowder, the black steed, and the goblin rider, passed by like a whirlwind.

Next morning old Gunpowder was found without his saddle, and with the bridle under his feet, soberly cropping grass at his master's gate. Ichabod did not make his appearance at breakfast; dinner hour came, but no Ichabod. The boys assembled at the schoolhouse and strolled idly along the brook; but no schoolmaster.

Hans Van Ripper now began to feel uneasy about the fate of poor Ichabod and his saddle. After careful investigation they came upon his traces. In the road leading to the church was found the saddle trampled in the dirt. Tracks of horses' hooves deeply dented in the road and evidently made at furious speed were traced to the bridge. On the bank beyond, where the brook ran deep and black was found the unfortunate Ichabod's hat. And close beside it a shattered pumpkin!

The brook was searched, but the schoolmaster's body was not discovered.

The mysterious event caused much speculation at church the following Sunday. Knots of gazers and gossips collected in the churchyard, at the bridge, and at the spot where the hat and pumpkin had been found. Stories of Bones and many others were recalled and compared with the recent case. The people shook their heads and agreed that Ichabod had been carried off by the galloping Headless Horseman.

It is true that an old farmer who went down to New York several years later and from whom this account of the ghostly adventure was received, brought back news that Ichabod Crane was still alive. He had left the neighborhood partly through fear of the goblin and Hans Van Ripper, and partly because of having been dismissed by the heiress. He had moved to a distant part of the country and kept school and studied law and finally had been made a Justice of the Ten Pound Court.

Brom Bones, who shortly after his rival's disappearance led the blooming Katrina in triumph to the altar, was observed to look very knowing whenever the story of Ichabod was related. He always burst into a heavy hearty laugh at the mention of the pumpkin, which led some to suspect he knew more of the matter than he chose to tell.

The old country wives, however, who are the best judges of these matters, mantain to this day that Ichabod was spirited away by supernatural means. It is a favorite story told about the neighborhood round the winter evening fire. The bridge became more than ever an object of superstitious awe, and that may be the reason why the road has been altered to approach the church by the border of the mill pond. The deserted schoolhouse fell into decay and was reported to be haunted by the ghost of the unfortunate schoolmaster. The plowboy, loitering homeward of a still summer evening, has often fancied Ichabod's voice at a distance chanting a melancholy psalm tune among the tranquil solitudes of Sleepy Hollow.

—EXCERPTED BY MILDRED CORELL LUCKHARDT FROM *The Sketch Book*

BY WASHINGTON IRVING

The Ghosts

One dark evening, after sundown,
In her wigwam Laughing Water
Sat with old Nokomis, waiting
For the steps of Hiawatha
Homeward from the hunt returning.
   On their faces gleamed the firelight,
Painting them with streaks of crimson. . . .
And behind them crouched their shadows
In the corners of the wigwam,
And the smoke in wreaths above them
Climbed and crowded through the smoke-flue.
   Then the curtain of the doorway
From without was slowly lifted;
Brighter glowed the fire a moment
And a moment swerved the smoke-wreath,
As two women entered softly,
Passed the doorway uninvited,
Without word of salutation,
Without sign of recognition,
Sat down in the farthest corner,
Crouching low among the shadows.
   From their aspect and their garments,

Strangers seemed they in the village;
Very pale and haggard were they,
As they sat there sad and silent,
Trembling, cowering with the shadows.
   Was it the wind above the smoke-flue,
Muttering down into the wigwam?
Was it the owl, the Koko-koho,
Hooting from the dismal forest?
Sure, a voice said in the silence:
"These are corpses clad in garments,
These are ghosts that come to haunt you,
From the Kingdom of Ponemah,
From the land of the Hereafter!"
   Homeward now came Hiawatha
From his hunting in the forest,
With the snow upon his tresses,
And the red deer on his shoulders.
At the feet of Laughing Water
Down he threw his lifeless burden;
Nobler, handsomer she thought him
Than when first he came to woo her,
First threw down the deer before her,
As a token of his wishes,
As a promise of the future.
   Then he turned and saw the strangers,
Cowering, crouching with the shadows;
Said within himself, "Who are they?
What strange guests has Minnehaha?"
But he questioned not the strangers,
Only spake to bid them welcome

To his lodge, his food, his fireside.
    When the evening meal was ready,
And the deer had been divided,
Both the pallid guests, the strangers,
Springing from among the shadows,
Seized upon the choicest portions,
Seized the white fat of the roebuck,
Set apart for Laughing Water,
For the wife of Hiawatha;
Without asking, without thanking,
Eagerly devoured the morsels,
Flitted back among the shadows
In the corner of the wigwam.
    Not a word spake Hiawatha,
Not a motion made Nokomis,
Not a gesture Laughing Water;
Not a change came o'er their features;
Only Minnehaha softly
Whispered, saying, "They are famished;
Let them do what best delights them;
Let them eat, for they are famished."
Many a daylight dawned and darkened,
Many a night shook off the daylight
As the pine shakes off the snow-flakes
From the midnight of its branches;
Day by day the guests unmoving
Sat there silent in the wigwam;
But by night, in storm or starlight,
Forth they went into the forest,
Bringing fire-wood to the wigwam,

Bringing pine-cones for the burning,
Always sad and always silent.

. . . .

Once at midnight Hiawatha,
Ever wakeful, ever watchful,
In the wigwam, dimly lighted
By the brands that still were burning,
By the glimmering, flickering firelight,
Heard a sighing, oft repeated,
Heard a sobbing, as of sorrow.
From his couch rose Hiawatha,
From his shaggy hides of bison,
Pushed aside the deer-skin curtain,
Saw the pallid guests, the shadows,
Sitting upright on their couches,
Weeping in the silent midnight.
And he said: "O guests! why is it
That your hearts are so afflicted,
That you sob so in the midnight?
Has perchance the old Nokomis,
Has my wife, my Minnehaha,
Wronged or grieved you by unkindness,
Failed in hospitable duties?"
Then the shadows ceased from weeping,
Ceased from sobbing and lamenting,
And they said, with gentle voices:
"We are the ghosts of the departed,
Souls of those who once were with you.
From the realms of Chibiabos
Hither have we come to try you,

Hither have we come to warn you.
   "Cries of grief and lamentation
Reach us in the Blessed Islands;
Cries of anguish from the living,
Calling back their friends departed,
Sadden us with useless sorrow.
Therefore, have we come to try you;
No one knows us, no one heeds us.
We are but a burden to you,
And we see that the departed
Have no place among the living.
   "Think of this, O Hiawatha!
Speak of it to all the people,
That henceforward and forever
They no more with lamentations
Sadden the souls of the departed
In the Islands of the Blessed.

   .   .   .   .

   "Farewell, noble Hiawatha!
We have put you to the trial,
To the proof have put your patience,
By the insult of our presence,
By the outrage of our actions.
We have found you great and noble.
Fail not in the greater trial,
Faint not in the harder struggle."
   When they ceased, a sudden darkness
Fell and filled the silent wigwam.
Hiawatha heard a rustle

As of garments trailing by him,
Heard the curtain of the doorway
Lifted by a hand he saw not,
Felt the cold breath of the night air,
For a moment saw the starlight;
But he saw the ghosts no longer,
Saw no more the wandering spirits
From the Kingdom of Ponemah,
From the Land of the Hereafter.

—LINES FROM *Hiawatha* BY
HENRY WADSWORTH LONGFELLOW

The Wishing Stone
(*A Celtic Tale*)

Mrs. Crony was on her way to the wishing stone. She passed, just at twilight, the church on the hill, and the sun was red on the high golden cross. She passed, just at dusk, the old stone bridge, and the shadows were huddled below listening to the whispers of the dark stream. She passed, just at fall of night, the Druid oak, and a white owl sat like an old lady hunched up on a long, twisted branch. Shivering, Mrs. Crony hurried by and went on through the low graveyard gate, by the silent stones and the silent mounds to the spot where the wishing stone squatted like a queer, silent toad.

A very slim, yellow sickle of a moon swung in the west with a blue star caught in its sweep. Mrs. Crony looked at it, shivered a little more, and said to herself, "This is the night; for the sickle of the new moon has cut down a forget-me-not in the gardens of heaven. Surely this night the promise will come true. Sometime between moonrise and sunrise a wish will be granted." So saying, Mrs. Crony began to wish.

"May my son become a king!" she cried softly. "May my son become a king!"

Without the loss of a second, she wished on and on till the new moon swung under the cross on the church. Just then queer, ghostly figures danced on the green off to the right.

"I will not be frightened by all the dancing worries in the world," said Mrs. Crony, and she repeated faster than ever, "may my son become a king!"

She wished on and on until the new moon swung under the long, twisted branch of the Druid oak. Just then the white owl ruffled his feathers and blinked his glowing red eyes.

"I will not be frightened by all the terrors in the world," said Mrs. Crony and she repeated faster than ever, "may my son become a king!"

She wished on and on until the new moon swung level with her eyes. Just then pale lights rose out of the marsh below and joined long, drooping arms and danced back and forth very, very slowly between the stems of the tall reeds.

"I will not be led away by all the false promises in the world," said Mrs. Crony and she repeated faster than ever, "may my son become a king!"

Just then the new moon went under a cloud, and the cross on the church was no more to be seen, and the Druid oak looked snaky against the sky, and the pale fires danced on in the marsh below. Something stirred close to Mrs. Crony. Something white moved slowly toward her. It had cloven feet and twisted horns and eyes that glowed like dying coals. Mrs. Crony clutched her shawl over her breast and stared. The white thing came to her very knees and laid its silver whiskers in her lap. "May the Old Harry break your neck!" cried Mrs. Crony, and just as she said the words the wishing time had come. Her wish was granted. Her poor old faithful goat fell down dead with his neck broken right off close to his shoulders.

Mrs. Crony groaned. "Sure it's an unlucky woman I am," she said, "to be led away from my good wishes by a poor old goat. I didn't mind the dancing worries, nor the ruffled terrors, nor the lying promises in the marsh; not one of these did I mind. Sure the cause of my failure came out of my own dooryard. I raised it with my own hand. I taught it to follow me about, and it has followed me here to the wishing stone and broken up the chain of my wishes just at the wrong time."

With that Mrs. Crony slung the goat over her left shoulder and, with her right hand clutching the horn of the goat's head, went back beneath the Druid oak and over the low bridge and under the cross to her own thatched home at the bend of the road.

—JOSEPH BURKE EGAN

Dolph Heyliger and the Haunted House

In the early time of the province of New York, there lived a kind motherly dame known as Dame Heyliger. She was the widow of a Dutch sea captain who died suddenly leaving her very little money and one infant son. She struggled to make both ends meet for herself and the little boy, Dolph. One day her neighbors were surprised to see that she had turned the front room of her house into a little shop. In her window appeared gingerbread men and sugar plums, barley sugar, Holland dolls, and other toys. At the door sat the good dame's cat, looking at everyone who passed by.

Although the good woman had come to this humble means of making a living, she still had family pride, for she was descended from the Vander Spiegels of Amsterdam and their coat of arms hung over her mantelpiece. Her son, Dolph, could not be called a comfort for he was the most mischievous urchin. She had constant complaints of pranks he had played, and she always was paying for windows Dolph had broken. Many neighbors called him wicked.

135

Yet the poor old mother loved her boy, and he was strongly attached to her and would not willingly have given her pain. But he was heedless and could not resist any fun and mischief. He had made such a reputation that when he was old enough to work no one seemed to employ him.

Dame Heylinger often talked about Dolph with her old friend Peter de Groodt, the clerk and sexton of the church, but for a long while he could think of no place where Dolph might learn a trade by which he could earn his living. At last, Peter was able to persuade the learned Doctor Karl Lodovick Knipperhausen to take him into the doctor's home and teach him until he was twenty-one. Doctor Knipperhausen was unlike other doctors, for he made up mysterious compounds and consulted the stars. It was thought there was no end to his knowledge.

Soon Dolph was up to his ears in medical studies from morning until night, rolling pills, filtering tinctures, pounding the pestle and mortar, while the doctor poured over a book. Often the little man was lulled to sleep by the thumping of Dolph's pestle. The doctor and Dolph were ruled by the busy, fretty housekeeper named Frau Ilsé (or Frow Ilsy, as it was pronounced). She was a prying gossip and spread stories about people's secret business. Between the doctor and the housekeeper Dolph had no easy life, and if he offended her he was almost starved at mealtime. Besides that she kept him running errands constantly.

Meanwhile, Dolph made slow progress in learning the doctor's profession, even though the doctor kept him hard at work. The fact is, Dolph was more fond of mischief and sport.

All the while the doctor waxed wealthy and renowned, and was reported to have cured several women of witchcraft. As he became wealthier he purchased a country home, a farm not far from town. It had been the residence of a wealthy family that had returned some time since to Holland. The large mansion house in the center of it was very much out of repair and was reported to be haunted. Because of this the doctor found it impossible to get a tenant. So that the place would not fall into ruin before he could retire there, he placed a country boor with his family in one wing, with the privilege of farming on shares.

The doctor now assumed the dignity of a landholder, and was fond of riding out "to look at his estate." His expeditions to look at his land were attended with a bustle and parade that created a sensation throughout the neighborhood. And when the doctor would return he was more irritable, for he always heard from the countryman at his farm some new complaint about strange noises and fearful sights with which his farm tenants were disturbed at night. The countryman threatened to leave, and this would mean a loss of all profits on the property. Then, what a blow to the doctor's pride, to be the owner of a haunted house!

It was observed that the doctor never remained there after dark, but made his way back to town as soon as bats began to flit in the twilight. All the while tales were spreading about the haunted house. When the tenant family left suddenly no one would stay there. All this put the doctor in a terrible state until Dolph boldly offered to stay each night at the haunted place. He now was nearly twenty-one, the term of his medical studies was nearly over, and he loved adventure. The doctor quickly said Dolph should mount guard that very night, and at Dolph's request promised that no one would tell Dolph's mother. Dolph was sure that she would not sleep a wink if she knew her son was waging war with the powers of darkness.

When night came on he set out on his perilous expedition, escorted by the doctor and Peter de Groodt, who would go with him to the house and see him safely lodged. The night was very dark and overcast when they arrived at the grounds surrounding the mansion. Peter led the way with a lantern, and the doctor clutched Dolph's arm. The front door opened with a grating sound, making the doctor turn pale. They went up a wide staircase that groaned and creaked. The room where Dolph was to sleep had a few pieces of broken furniture, and in the center stood a heavy table and large old armchair.

While Peter lighted the rushlight on the table, the doctor looked fearfully about and was telling Dolph to be of good cheer when a noise in the chimney struck a sudden panic in him and Peter. They fled with the lantern.

Left alone, Dolph bolted and barred the front door, and, having seen that all other entrances were fastened, returned to his desolate bedroom, locked the door and lay down to rest on a mattress in one corner. The rushlight shed a feeble yellow ray, making uncouth shadows on the wall. Dolph felt low-spirited as he gazed about the gloomy room. By and by he thought he heard someone walking downstairs. Then, a step on the stairs! It approached solemnly, slowly—tramp, tramp, tramp! It was evidently the step of some heavy person. Yet how could he have got into the house without making noise since every entrance was secure? Still the steps advanced—tramp, tramp, tramp!

Now the steps came along the hall. The door, which had been locked on the inside, slowly swung open. The footsteps entered the room. But no one was to be seen. The steps tramped slowly across the room! Yet whatever made the sound was invisible. Dolph stared into every part of the dimly lighted room. All was vacant, yet he heard those mysterious footsteps solemnly walking about it. They ceased, and all was dead silence. Dolph's heart beat hard against his ribs, a cold sweat broke out on his forehead. He lay for some time in dread, but nothing further happened. Then the light burned down, and at last he fell asleep.

When he awoke, the sun was peering through the cracks of the shutters, and birds were singing merrily. Dolph tried to forget the terrors of the night and to laugh and tell himself that he imagined the happenings because of the stories he had heard. He was puzzled to find the door of his room locked from the inside, since he had seen it swing open when the footsteps entered. He returned to town determined to say nothing on the subject until after another night's watching. The gossips who had gathered at the doctor's, prepared to hear dreadful tales, were almost in a rage when he said he had nothing to tell.

The next night Dolph entered the haunted house with fear and fastened all doors. He locked the door of his room and placed a chair against it. Then, after eating the supper he had brought, he threw himself on the mattress and tried to sleep. It was all in vain—as the night advanced he grew more and more nervous. He jumped in fright when the mysterious tramp—tramp—tramp came up the stairs and along the hall to his door. The door swung open, and in stalked a large elderly man dressed in the old Flemish fashion of many years before.

He walked slowly around the room. Then, after hanging his hat on a peg beside the door, he sat in the chair and fixed his eyes on Dolph with a deadening stare. Dolph was not a coward, but he had been brought up in a firm belief in ghosts and goblins. As he looked at this strange personage, with uncouth garb, pale visage, and staring fishlike eye, Dolph's teeth began to chatter. How long he lay staring at this specter he could not tell. The old man stayed seated behind the table, keeping a dead steady glare upon Dolph.

At length the crow of a cock from a nearby farm rang over the fields, and the old man rose and put on his hat. The door swung open and closed after him, and Dolph lay and listened to the tramp of the feet going slowly down the stairs. At last, when they did not return, he fell into a troubled sleep.

Daylight brought Dolph fresh courage. The door and the chair in front of it were as he had left them last night; downstairs windows and doors were locked. There seemed no way whereby the house could have been entered and no trace that anyone had left. "Pooh!" Dolph told himself, "it was all a dream!" But he could not shake the scene from his mind.

Although he was silent when he returned to town, Dolph's looks showed that he had spent an uncomfortable night. Each one in turn, from the doctor to Frau Ilsy to Peter de Groodt, and then the different neighbors, tried to get him to talk about the night's mysterious happenings, but he told nothing. Soon the neighborhood was full of wild reports, and all sorts of tales were told about the legion of ghosts that had threatened Dolph.

When the rumors reached good Dame Heyliger, she hastened to the doctor's house and begged Dolph not to go to the haunted house again. He tried to calm her and told her there was no truth in the rumors.

So, at night he took up his quarters for the third time in the old mansion. Once again, toward midnight the same tramp—tramp— tramp echoed through the halls and up the stairs. The door swung open and the old man entered and hung up his hat. Dolph watched trembling when the specter seated himself and stared at him with a chilling gaze for a long time. It occurred to Dolph that this specter might have some purpose for this visit, and he had heard that spirits have no power to speak until spoken to.

Summoning all his courage, Dolph demanded to know from the unknown what was the motive of his visit. At once the old man rose and put on his hat. The door opened, and he went out, looking back upon Dolph as if expecting him to follow. Trembling, Dolph followed the figure downstairs and toward the back door. When he reached it the unknown had disappeared, and the door remained locked. Dolph unlocked the door and peered into the hazy moonlight night. The unknown was moving along a footpath that led from this door. Dolph followed along the footpath, through the orchard, down to a well. When Dolph reached the well, nothing was to be seen of the specter, nothing at all.

Dolph looked down the well and saw, at great depth, the reflection of the sky in the still water. After waiting alone for some time he returned to the house, full of awe and wonder. He bolted the door, groped back to bed, and it was very long before he fell into troubled sleep.

In a strange dream, he thought he followed the specter beside a great river until they came to a boat on the point of sailing. The mysterious old man led Dolph aboard and vanished. The commander of the vessel was short, swarthy, black-haired, blind of one eye, lame of one leg. The rest of the dream was confused. Sometimes Dolph was sailing, sometimes on shore, now amid storms, now wandering on unknown streets, with the old man throughout the dream. It wound up with Dolph's returning home on that boat with a great bag of money.

When he awoke he was more perplexed than ever and even wondered whether his mind was affected. He could not return at once to the doctor's and undergo the cross-examination there. So, after eating the remains of his food, he wandered gradually toward town. After a time, he found himself near the water's edge in a throng of people hurrying to a pier where a vessel was just ready to sail up the Hudson to Albany.

The sloop's commander caught Dolph's attention. He looked like the commander in his dream! The boat was like the one in his dream, too! As he stood staring, the captain told him, "Step aboard, young man, or you'll be left behind!" Startled, Dolph sprang on deck and the sloop was hurried off by wind and tide. He felt under supernatural influence. Surely there was a connection between this and his dream. Dolph felt he had nothing to lose, and determined to enjoy the voyage.

When, on the second day, they came to the highlands, he gazed in delight at their magnificence. Yet, even as they neared Dunderberg where the goblin storm king lived, thunder rolled over the mountains, the wind curled up the waves, lightning leaped from cloud to cloud and streamed quivering against the rocks, while torrents of rain rattled down. Just as they turned a point, wind swept down a mountain gully, struck the sails and threw the sloop on her beam ends. In the confusion of righting the boat, the boom swept the quarter-deck and threw Dolph into the river. No one saw him go, and the sloop was driven around a bend of the river.

Although a strong swimmer, Dolph struggled to reach the western shore. Faint and exhausted he threw himself on the ground and lay quivering until, at last, the storm passed over. Then began the toilsome, painful, frightening climb up jagged rocks, upward from the shore. At last he succeeded in scrambling to the summit of a precipice, from which he could see nothing but the river far below and dense forest, and a darkly wooded ravine. His foot dislodged a rock and it crashed through treetops into the chasm below. A yell rose from the glen, followed by a gun shot, and a ball whistled over his head and buried itself in a nearby tree.

Dolph fled for cover, then made his way back to the shore. He sat down, dripping and dejected, on a wet stone. Night closed in, gloomy and still. Suddenly he saw a light gleaming through the trees near the shore. Hungry and chilled through, he made his way along until he came to a hunting party of white men and Indians near a campfire. He hallooed the Indian friendship salutation. The party sprang to their feet and invited him to join them.

Their leader introduced himself as Antony Vander Heyden from Albany, of whom Dolph had heard. Heer Vander Heyden had inherited large tracts of wild land and barrels of wampum. He was a grand friend to Indians, and was never so happy as when out in the wilderness. He was highly respected wherever he went.

While Dolph shared in their hearty meal, he told his story of being knocked overboard. Heer Antony welcomed him to sail with him to Albany, since he and some of the party were returning to his home there the next morning. Later, as the fire died down, different ones told legends of supernatural happenings in these highlands, since it was thought that mischievous beings had taken a dislike to the early Dutch colonists and now took out their spite on the Dutch skippers. It was agreed that Dolph might have been tossed overboard by some such beings.

Tales were told of the mysterious Stormship, which had haunted the river for generations and was always a sign of impending trouble for Dutch people. This phantom ship and its passengers were bedeviled by the frightening goblin king of the Dunderberg, the thunder mountain. Dolph had heard many of these stories before, and their spell was upon him now as Heer Antony recalled the tales. With the firelight gleaming on the strong older man's face, Dolph saw a strange resemblance to the phantom of the haunted house—not the precise features but a similarity of face and figure.

During the next few days they coasted along pleasantly on their voyage. Dolph and Heer Antony came to understand each other and to develop a good friendship. When Dolph was invited to go to the Vander Heyden home, he felt that, somehow, all his recent experiences were connected with the Haunted House.

On their arrival in Albany, everyone seemed to know Antony Vander Heyden and greet his return happily. Dolph was welcomed into the home with the master, and soon was enjoying an abundant evening meal planned by Heer Antony's lovely daughter, Marie. During the evening when many neighbors dropped in to hear about Heer Antony's expedition, Dolph and Marie sat on the window bench and talked. He could feel himself falling in love. But afterward in his room he decided he must leave his hearty host and pretty hostess and cast himself once more adrift in the world. To linger here would be folly—he would get deeper in love, and it was madness for a poor varlet like himself to aspire to marry the daughter of the great Heer Vander Heyden.

As he got into bed and reached out to extinguish the candle, he was struck with dismay, for he thought he saw the phantom of the haunted house gazing at him from a dusky part of the room. Staring, he saw it was a Flemish portrait. But, it was the precise picture of his ghostly visitor! Awestruck, he finally put out the light. Then in his dreams the figure in the picture descended from the wall and walked from the room. Dolph followed and found himself at the well, to which the old man pointed, smiled on him and disappeared.

The next morning Dolph inquired about the portrait, and Heer Antony replied, "That is of old Killian Vander Spiegel, once a burgomaster of Amsterdam, who came over here during the government of Peter Stuyvesant. He was an ancestor on my mother's side, an old miser. When the English took New Amsterdam he retired to the country, turned his property into cash, and hid his money. After he died no one could discover where he had hidden most of it."

Dolph thought this over for some time after Heer Antony left the room. He remembered that his mother had spoken of Killian Vander Spiegel as one of her ancestors, and that her father was his heir, but the old man had died leaving nothing. Dolph thought that this all might be an interpretation of his dream. But why had the old goblin used such a roundabout way of sending him to Albany first and then all the way back again?

Dolph walked down the stairs, perplexed. When Marie's smile beamed on him, he thought, "The old goblin is right." If Dolph married Marie, as he hoped he might, then both branches of the family would be united and the property would go on in the right channel without anyone's being defrauded.

Two or three days passed before he could board a boat going down the river. All the while he became more enamored with Marie. Both she and her father tried to persuade him to remain, but he told them it was necessary to go. At length he sailed away on the very sloop from which he had been knocked overboard. The wind was fair, and they soon lost sight of Albany.

Within a few days they sailed to the wharf of Manhattan Island. Dolph sprang from the boat and hastened to his mother's house, thinking of the uneasiness she had suffered because of him. How could he account for his absence without betraying the secrets of the haunted house? When he entered the street where his mother's house had stood, he was thunderstruck to find that several houses, including hers, had been completely destroyed by fire. As he faced the ruins, fearful that his mother might have perished, a neighbor told him she was alive. Peter de Groodt, poor as he was, had given her and her cat shelter.

As Dolph approached Peter's house, the old man, just coming out, started back aghast, thinking he was a ghost, for Dolph had been given up as dead. It had been universally believed that Dolph had been spirited away by the goblins of the haunted house.

In the joy of her son's return, Dame Heyliger forgot all her troubles. But she worried about what would become of him since she could help him no longer.

Meanwhile, news was carried to Doctor Knipperhausen of his pupil's return. Frau Ilse advised him to shut the door on Dolph forever. So that night when Dolph raised the knocker with a faltering hand, both the doctor and Frau Ilse greeted him with a volley of hard names and hard language. Soon from every window in the street a nightcap appeared, with everyone listening and spreading the word, "Dolph Heyliger is back, and at his old pranks again." Dolph beat a retreat and spent the night under the lowly roof of honest Peter de Groodt.

Early the next morning Dolph was at the haunted house. With palpitating heart he hastened to the well. Looking down, he saw it was very deep, with water at the bottom. He had brought a strong line such as fishermen use on the Newfoundland banks. At the end was a heavy plummet and a large fish-hook. With this he sounded the bottom of the well and angled about in the water. The water was of some depth. Much rubbish and stones from the top had fallen in. Several times his hook got entangled, and he came near breaking his line. Now and then he hauled up trash, a horse's skull, an iron hoop, a shattered iron-bound bucket. After several hours he had found nothing to encourage him to go on. He began to think himself a fool, decoyed into a wild-goose chase by dreams, and was on the point of throwing line and all into the well and giving up further angling.

"One more cast of the line," said he, "and that shall be the last."

As he sounded, he felt the plummet slip through spaces among the loose stones. The line took hold of something heavy. He had to manage with great caution, lest the line be broken by the strain on it. By degrees, the rubbish that lay on the article he had hooked gave way, and he drew it to the surface. What was his rapture at seeing something like silver glittering at the end of the line! Breathless with anxiety, he drew it up to the mouth of the well, surprised at its great weight, and fearing that his hook would slip and his prize tumble again to the bottom.

At length he landed it safe beside the well. It was a great silver porringer of ancient form, richly embossed and with armorial bearings similar to those over his mother's mantelpiece engraved on its side. The lid was fastened down by several twists of wire. Dolph loosened them with a trembling hand. On lifting the lid, behold! the vessel was filled with broad golden pieces of a coinage he never had seen. He had lit on the place where Killian Vander Spiegel had concealed his treasure!

Fearful of being seen, Dolph buried the money in a secret place. He now spread terrible stories about the haunted house, while he made frequent visits to it on stormy nights when no one was stirring in the neighboring fields.

Gradually he managed to bring his property into use without exciting inquiry, and he satisfied all scruples about keeping it. And, in time, he married the pretty Marie Vander Heyden. He took his mother to live in their home and cherished her in her old days. The good dame now had the satisfaction of hearing her son spoken well of. And Peter de Groodt, as he sat by the fireside with one of her grandchildren on his knee, would many a time congratulate her upon her son turning out so great a man. Then the good old soul would exclaim, "Ah, neighbor, did I not say that Dolph would one day hold up his head with the best of them?"

—ADAPTED BY MILDRED CORELL LUCKHARDT
from *Bracebridge Hall* BY WASHINGTON IRVING

The Dead Ship of Harpswell

What flecks the outer gray beyond
  The sundown's golden trail?
The white flash of a sea-bird's wing,
  Or gleam of slanting sail?
Let young eyes watch from Neck and Point,
  And sea-worn elders pray,—
The ghost of what was once a ship
  Is sailing up the bay!

From gray sea-fog, from icy drift,
  From peril and from pain,
The home-bound fisher greets thy lights,
  O hundred-harbored Maine!
But many a keel shall seaward turn,
  And many a sail outstand,
When, tall and white, the Dead Ship looms
  Against the dusk of land.
. . . .

What weary doom of baffled quest,
  Thou sad sea-ghost, is thine?
What makes thee in the haunts of home
  A wonder and a sign?
No foot is on thy silent deck,

Upon thy helm no hand;
No ripple hath the soundless wind
That smites thee from the land!

For never comes the ship to port,
Howe'er the breeze may be;
Just when she nears the waiting shore,
She drifts again to sea.
No tack of sail, nor turn of helm,
Nor sheer of veering side;
Stern-fore she drives to sea and night,
Against the wind and tide.

In vain o'er Harpswell Neck the star
Of evening guides her in;
In vain for her the lamps are lit
Within thy tower, Seguin!
In vain the harbor-boat shall hail,
In vain the pilot call;
No hand shall reef her spectral sail,
Or let her anchor fall.

—JOHN GREENLEAF WHITTIER

Ghostly Gold

Ghosts often are found protecting lost loot, missing fortunes, hidden treasure. Such a ghostly protector guarded a cache of gold at a sawmill in a valley by a stream near Grandfather Mountain, North Carolina. The turbulent mountain stream had been halted in the valley by a shallow dam. The cold dark pool behind the dam was released gradually to drive the whining blades of the mill that sawed trees from the mountain into lumber.

The ghost who haunted the mill was that of a stranger who came to the valley one day on foot, traveling north. Nobody knew anything about him. He carried a canvas bag filled with something very heavy. Some thought it might be gold. He spent a night at the mill and never was seen again after sunset, nor known to leave next morning. Tales spread around that he had been killed during the night for the gold he carried and that his body had been weighted and hidden in the deep, dark millpond.

From then on people began to hear blood-curdling sounds and

shiverings when they passed the mill on nights when there was no moon. They said the ghost rose from the cold mountain water, shook terribly, and went about his job of ghosting and haunting.

One night a native of the hills, Dave Kinder, took an extra slug of corn likkar and announced he wasn't afraid of tthat mill ghost and was going to the mill just to see what a ghost is like. He took a lantern and some matches but didn't plan to strike a light until he heard something to make it worth while.

Sure enough, that shivering noise they all had heard struck up after a while. Although Dave was waiting for it, the sound made his hair rise up and stand straight up on his head. It was the "awfulest" noise and he was close to it. Then there was a rattling noise around his feet that scared him even more. But in a few seconds he realized it was the sulphur matches falling one by one from his trembling hands. He recovered a match, struck a light in the lantern, and then he almost died of fright.

The shivering noise had stopped. Something was coming straight toward him! Slow, measured footsteps came nearer, nearer. The footfalls stopped almost beside him! Dave mustered strength to open his eyes. There stood the terrible sight of the dripping remains of the drowned man.

The apparition beckoned Dave to follow and walked off into the brush on the side of the wall. There the awful thing pointed to a spot on the ground among vines and low underbrush. Dave took one look, found his running feet at the end of tottering legs, and moved away fast.

He burst into his home, panting for breath, cried out to his wife, "I'm drunk! I got chills and shakes, and I want to lie down."

After getting into bed, still shaking with fright, he told his wife what happened. She was delighted and said, "You're not drunk.

You've stumbled into a fortune. The ghost was trying to tell you where the money is buried. Get a good sleep, and in the morning I'll help you dig at the spot the ghost showed you."

Early next morning with his wife at the mill, Dave was able to locate the very spot the ghost had pointed out. Maybe he hadn't been drunk and maybe his wife had been right. He stuck his mattock into the earth while his wife looked on. But as he whammed into matted vines and began to turn up the dark earth, the ground around them began to tremble violently. They were so scared they ran for their lives.

They never returned for a second try. Dave said that in the following months whenever he rode by the mill, something seemed to try to pull him off his horse and up toward the spot in the honeysuckle vines. Terrified, he'd always lash his horse and flee. Dave said he'd like to have the money, but not that bad. He wanted to live more than he wanted gold. His wife agreed.

—JOHN HARDEN

The Ghost of Captain Brand

Barnaby True was a good, honest lad, but he was not allowed ever to forget that his grandfather had been the famous pirate, Captain William Brand, who, after many marvelous adventures, was murdered in Jamaica by Captain John Malyoe, the commander of his own consort, the *Adventure* galley. When Captain Brand started on that adventure it was with the ship *Royal Sovereign,* fitted out by decent New York merchants. The governor subscribed to the adventure, so if Captain Brand went astray he must have had great temptation.

When Barnaby was nearly seventeen he started to work in the countinghouse of his kind stepfather, Mr. Roger Hartright, well-known West India merchant. Through Mr. Hartright's kindness, Barnaby was advanced quickly and before age twenty-one had made four voyages as supercargo to the West Indies in the ship *Belle Helen.* Soon after Barnaby was twenty-one he became Mr. Hartright's confidential agent and went on his fifth voyage to the West Indies.

155

There he stayed for about four weeks in a lodging house in Kingston.

One morning during breakfast Barnaby received a mysterious, surprising note. It told him to be at Pratt's Ordinary (a tavern by the harbor) on Friday night at eight o'clock. A man there would say to him, "The *Royal Sovereign* is come in," and he was to go with that man to learn information of great value. He must take the note with him to Pratt's so the stranger could be sure he was Barnaby True. No name or address was on this astonishing letter.

Barnaby was so amazed that he decided to show it to Mr. Greenfield, a trustworthy man with whom he did business for Mr. Hartright while in Jamaica. Mr. Greenfield thought the whole thing was some kind of prank. Barnaby agreed, but decided to see it through, so he went a little early on Friday night to Pratt's. He walked to a table at the end of the garden by the water's edge, where he could not be seen easily by anyone coming into the place. Many vessels, including a big man-of-war, lay at anchor in the harbor, but Barnaby saw nothing that might concern the note.

After a while a rowboat appeared suddenly out of the night and pulled to the landing at the foot of the garden. Several men came ashore in the darkness. Without a word they chose a nearby table, ordered rum and water, and began drinking in silence. By and by, Barnaby became aware that they were observing him very curiously. Then their leader called to him:

"How now, messmate! Won't you come and drink a dram of rum with us?"

"Why, no," says Barnaby. "I have drunk enough already."

"All the same," quoth the stranger, "I think you will come and drink with us; for, unless I am mistook, you are Mr. Barnaby True, and I am come to tell you that the *Royal Sovereign is come in.*"

Barnaby was never more struck aback. He had been expecting

to hear those words under different circumstances, and now that his ears heard them addressed to him so seriously by a perfect stranger who had mysteriously come ashore out of the darkness, he could scarce believe that he heard aright. His heart began beating at a tremendous rate. He contrived, however, to say in as easy a tone as he could put on, "If the *Royal Sovereign* is indeed come in, I'll join you since you are so kind as to ask me." He went to the other table, carrying his pipe, and sat down and began smoking with all the appearance of ease he could assume, while the man began speaking in a low tone.

"I am glad to see you are man enough to enter into an affair, though you can't see to the bottom of it; and you are deserving of the fortune that is to befall you tonight. First, though, I am bid to say you must show me a piece of paper you have with you."

While Barnaby handed him the mysterious note, he drew the candle toward him. Barnaby saw he was tall and stout, with a red handkerchief tied around his neck and with copper buckles on his shoes. He burned the note with the candle after reading it.

"Barnaby True," he continued, "I was sent to ask if you're man enough to take your life in your hands and go with me in that boat down there? Say 'Yes,' and we'll start away at once, for the devil

is ashore here in Jamaica and if he gets ahead of us we may whistle
for what we're after. Say 'No,' and I go away, and you shall never
be troubled again in this sort."

If Barnaby's courage wavered a moment, it was not for long,
and he spoke up with a steady voice. "To be sure I'm man enough
to go with you and if you mean me harm I can look out for myself;
and here is something can look out for me." He showed the butt
of a pistol.

The man assured him he meant Barnaby no harm and said, "If
you have to use that barker 'twill not be upon us, your friends, but
upon one more wicked than the devil himself. Come, let us get away."

He and Barnaby and the others who had not spoken a word
went down to the boat. It was a large yawl with ten men for rowers.
In the stern sheets were two lanterns, and there were several iron
shovels. When everyone was in the boat it was shoved off, and the
rowers pulled straight out into the harbor and, after some distance,
rowed around the stern of the man-of-war. They all might have
been ghosts for the silence of the party in the yawl, and Barnaby
was too full of serious thoughts to talk.

After almost an hour they drew near the mouth of the Rio
Cobra River. Barnaby recognized the low point of land with a long
row of coconut palms. The rowers pulled strongly against the out-
going tide, but still no one said a word as to the business at hand.
Barnaby had the feeling it was a dream as the boat came slowly
around from under a clump of mangrove bushes and into open water
again. Suddenly the leader called out sharply, and the rowers instantly
lay on their oars. Barnaby became aware that another boat was
coming downriver where they lay, now drifing with the tide out
into the harbor again, and because of that boat their captain had
ordered his men to stop rowing.

The other boat, as well as he could see in the distance, was full
of men. Even in the darkness moonlight glimmered on the barrels of
muskets or pistols; and Barnaby heard the chug! chug! of oars louder and louder through the watery stillness of night as the boat drew
nearer. He had no idea whether these were friends or enemies or
what would happen next.

When the other boat came close to Barnaby's, a man in the
stern ordered his oarsmen to stop. Then he stood up. As they passed
by the moonlight shone full upon him. He was a large, stout gentleman with a round, red face, and clad in a fine laced red coat.
Amidship of that boat was a chest covered with cakes of sand and
dirt. In passing, the gentleman pointed at it with his elegant gold-
headed cane. "Are you come after this, Abraham Dawling?" said he,
with an evil grin.

The leader in the boat with Barnaby sat still as stone. Then,
at last, he appeared to regain his wits and bawled after the other boat
as it went by, "Very well, Jack Malyoe! You've got ahead of us this
time again, and next time is the third and it shall be our turn even
if William Brand must come back from hell to settle with you."

The fine gentleman made no reply as they passed by except to
burst into a roaring fit of laughter. Among the armed men in the
stern of the passing boat was a lean villainous one who flourished a
big pistol and shouted, "Do but give me the word, Your Honor,
and I'll put another bullet through the son of a sea cook." But the
gentleman forbade him, and the boat was gone into the night.

As Barnaby's boat went back to shore the captain fell a-cursing.
Barnaby was so shaken by what he had heard and seen he was scarcely conscious of where he was when at last he was put ashore below
the old custom house. Bewildered, he walked toward his lodging
house, remembering the names he had heard. John Malyoe was captain of the *Adventure* and had shot Barnaby's grandfather, Captain

William Brand. Abraham Dawling was the gunner of the *Royal Sovereign* and had been shot at the same time with the pirate captain and with him left stretched out in the staring sun by the murderers.

This whole business tonight was so dark and mysterious it seemed part of another life, not Barnaby's. He could only guess what the mud-covered chest contained and what its finding meant.

Barnaby said nothing to a living soul about what he had seen that night, but he could think of little or nothing else for days after. Often when he visited at the home of Mr. Greenfield, Mr. Hartright's correspondent and agent in these parts, he strongly wanted to tell what had happened, but he would think better of it and remain silent.

Two days before the *Belle Helen* sailed from Kingston, Mr. Greenfield invited Barnaby to come to dinner to meet the chief passenger for New York and his granddaughter, Sir John Malyoe and Miss Marjorie Malyoe. "Did you ever hear of Captain Jack Malyoe?"

Although the question was like hitting Barnaby a blow, he was able to reply that he had heard of Captain Malyoe. Mr. Greenfield went on to explain that Jack Malyoe had been a desperate pirate twenty years ago, but he now was Sir John Malyoe, owner of a fine Devonshire estate. Although many people overlooked his past, his relatives turned a cold shoulder to him.

So that night Barnaby came face to face with the man who had murdered his grandfather. That other night in the harbor he had seen Sir John Malyoe at a distance in the dark. Now Barnaby thought he never had looked at a more evil face. Malyoe's eyes stood out like balls, red and watery, and he winked them continually as though they were smarting; his lips were thick and purple-red; and his fat, red cheeks were mottled with clots of purple veins. When he spoke his voice rattled so that one wished to clear one's own throat. He was wholly distasteful to Barnaby.

But Sir John Malyoe's granddaughter was the most lovely young lady Barnaby had ever seen. She seemed very afraid of Sir John and would shrink whenever he spoke to her, and she answered in a very low, timid voice.

As for Sir John, he gobbled dinner like a pig, and drank smacking his lips, but said hardly a word to his granddaughter or Mrs. Greenfield or Barnaby. A great bloated beast of a man!

Only after dinner when Marjorie and the two Greenfield misses sat in a corner together did Barnaby hear her talk with ease. She chatted at a great rate, though hardly above her breath, until suddenly her grandfather called in his hoarse, rattling voice, that it was time to go. She jumped up, frightened.

Barnaby and Mr. Greenfield went to see them into their coach, where Sir John's man stood holding the lantern. Who should the man be but the lean villain with bald head who had offered to shoot the leader of Barnaby's expedition out into the harbor that night!

The next day Sir John's belongings began to come aboard the *Belle Helen,* and that lean, villainous manservant came across the gangplank with two men behind him lugging a great sea chest. He said sarcastically that he thought Barnaby was more than supercargo when he saw him talking with Sir John last night, and ordered Barnaby to help set His Honor's cabin to rights.

To this impudent speech Barnaby replied, "You'll find the steward yonder; he'll show you the cabin," and walked away. Turning back he could see the fellow staring after him angrily, and he knew he had made an enemy who was not likely to forgive him.

The next day when Sir John and his follower came aboard and passed close by Barnaby he loked straight in Barnaby's face and showed no sign that he knew who the lad was. The manservant, directing four men who carried two heavy trunks, saw it all and fell to grinning to see Barnaby slighted.

Marjorie flushed red when passing Barnaby, and she bowed and smiled at him graciously. Then she recovered as though frightened.

Soon the *Belle Helen* sailed. Since Sir John stayed all the time in his cabin with those two trunks, it fell upon Barnaby to show attention to the young lady. And glad enough he was of the opportunity. As the days went by he fell more in love with her, and she seemed to like his company.

All went pleasantly until one evening. Barnaby and Marjorie had been standing together at the rail looking westward across the water when she began to tell sadly about her affairs. Her grandfather was taking her to New York and then on to Boston to meet her cousin Captain Malyoe, who was the next heir to the Devonshire estate. She and he were to be married in the fall.

Poor Barnaby stood staring across the ocean, stunned and wretched. She, poor thing, said in a low voice that she had liked him from the moment she saw him and always would remember him as a dear friend who had been very kind to her. When his tongue broke loose and he told her that he loved her and was sick at heart over what she had said of her forthcoming marriage, she answered softly that it only could be painful to them to speak of such things. She must do everything her grandfather bade her, for he was a terrible man.

At this sad moment, someone who had been hiding nearby suddenly moved away, and Barnaby could see in the gathering darkness that it was the villain manservant, who must have heard all. The man went straight to Sir John's great cabin, while Barnaby looked after him, bitterly wretched. Marjorie could not have seen the villain.

Suddenly Sir John ran from the cabin, without his hat, carrying his gold-headed cane, straight across the deck to where Barnaby and Marjorie stood. That spying wretch ran grinning at his heels.

Screaming insults at his granddaughter, Sir John waved his cane as if he would strike her. "Get to your cabin before I lay this cane across your shoulders. What do you do here with this Yankee supercargo, not fit for a gentlewoman to wipe her feet upon?"

Furiously angry, Barnaby pushed Sir John violently back, shouting at him for threatening a young lady and saying that for a farthing he would wrench the stick out of the man's hand and throw it overboard. Sir John staggered back, then caught himself up. Bellowing he ran at Barnaby, whirling his cane, and would have struck the young man had not the manservant held him back.

Barnaby cried, "Keep back! If you strike me with that stick I'll fling you overboard."

At that moment Captain Manly and the first mate came running out of the cabin, and some of the crew came hurrying up. But Barnaby could not stop himself, and cried out, "You may shoot a man from behind, as you shot poor Captain Brand on the Rio Cobra River, but you dare not strike me face to face. I know who you are and what you are!"

At this Sir John stood stock-still, his bulging eyes staring as though they would pop out of his head.

When Captain Manly wanted to know what it was all about, Barnaby answered vehemently, "The villain insulted me and the young lady, and then threatened to strike me. But I know what he's got in his cabin in those two trunks, and where he found it and who it belongs to. He found it on the shores of the Rio Cobra River, and I have only to open my mouth and tell what I know."

But Captain Manly told Barnaby very sternly that he should

go to his cabin no matter what the passenger had done. "Stay there till I tell you to come out again, and when we reach New York I'll tell your stepfather how you have behaved. I'll have no such rioting aboard my ship."

Barnaby looked around, but the young lady was gone. Sir John stood in the lantern light, his face white as ashes, with a dreadful, hateful stare fixed on Barnaby.

Despairing, humiliated, Barnaby went to his cabin. He lay for a long while staring into the darkness, then dozed into a light sleep, with horrid dreams. Suddenly he was aroused by the noise of a pistol shot and then another and another; then a great bump and a grinding jar, and many footsteps running across the deck and down into the great cabin. A tremendous uproar of voices came from that cabin, and the sound of struggling, as of men's bodies being tossed about and striking violently against partitions and bulkheads. Women screamed, and Sir John cried in the greatest extremity: "You villains!"

Barnaby snatched a pistol and dashed into the great cabin. It was black as night and full of uproar pierced by two women's voices screaming, one in the cabin and one in the stateroom beyond. Barnaby pitched headlong over some men struggling on the deck, but regained his pistol quickly.

Amid the uproar he heard Captain Manly's voice calling, "You bloody pirate, would you choke me to death?"

Suddenly, Barnaby realized they had been attacked by pirates. In the companionway he saw outlined against the darkness the shadowy form of a man's figure standing motionless as a statue, and he knew in a moment that that must be the master maker of this devil's brew. Barnaby covered the bosom of that silent figure with his pistol and pulled the trigger.

In a flash of red light and stunning report of the pistol shot, Barnaby saw a broad, flat face with fishy eyes, a lean, bony forehead with a great blotch of blood on the side, a cocked hat trimmed with gold lace, a red scarf across the breast, and the gleam of brass buttons. Then black darkness swallowed everything again.

In that instant Sir John shrieked, " 'Tis William Brand!" Therewith came the sound of someone falling down heavily.

The next moment, Barnaby's sight came back in the darkness, and he beheld that dark, motionless figure still standing exactly where it had stood before. So he knew either that he had missed it or else it was supernatural and a leaden bullet would do it no harm. Though it was an apparition, Barnaby saw it as plain as ever he saw a living man.

This was the last Barnaby knew, for somebody struck him such a violent blow that with a great humming in the head he swooned away. When Barnaby came to his senses again it was to find himself being cared for with great skill, his head being bathed with cold water, and a bandage being bound about it as carefully as though a surgeon were attending him.

He could not immediately recall what had happened. When he opened his eyes he saw, by the light of the lantern and the gray light of dawn, that he was in a strange cabin, well fitted and painted white and gold. Two men were bending over him—one, a Negro in striped shirt with a yellow handkerchief around his head, and silver earrings; the other, a white man in outlandish dress of foreign make, with gold earrings, and great mustachios hanging down. They were tending to Barnaby's hurt with extreme care and gentleness.

Remembering what had befallen him, and with his head beating as though it would split, Barnaby shut his eyes again, making a great effort to keep form groaning aloud. He wondered what sort

of pirates these could be who would first knock a man on the head
and then take such care to fetch him back to life and make him
comfortable. He lay there with his eyes closed until the bandage
was properly tied about his head and sewn together. Then once more
he opened his eyes and asked where he was.

Either they did not choose to reply or they could not speak
English. But the white man nodded his head several times and
smiled with a grin of white teeth and pointed as though toward a
saloon beyond. The Negro held up Barnaby's coat and beckoned
for him to put it on. So, seeing it was required of him to, meet
someone without, Barnaby arose with much effort, and the Negro
helped him on with his coat, although his head beat fit to split and
his legs were uncertain.

Still sick and dizzy he went into a fine saloon below. There at a
fine mahogany table sat the very man who had conducted the mysterious expedition across Kingston Harbor to the Rio Cobra River.

The man looked steadily at Barnaby then burst out laughing.
"And how does your head feel by now, my young master?"

Wondering and dizzy, Barnaby seated himself at the table,
and the man said, "You were treated ill that night, but I do not know
who cracked you upon the head. I'm sorry, for the way you were
handled, for nothing was meant to you but kindness."

Then he recalled to Barnaby their expedition into Kingston
Harbor and how he had said to Jack Malyoe that next time it would
be their turn even if William Brand himself had to come back from
hell to put the business through. Next he moved to one side and
showed Barnaby the two trunks that Sir John had fetched aboard
the Jamaica. Flinging back the lids the man displayed to Barnaby
a great treasure of gold and silver.

Barnaby was dumb struck!

The man continued, "It is not for the sake of showing you this that I have been waiting, but there is another passenger on board whom I am to confide to your care according to orders I have received. I shall fetch her in, if you are ready, Master Barnaby."

He went from the room and soon ushered in a young lady who came slowly into the saloon. It was Miss Marjorie Malyoe, very white and looking bewildered by all that had befallen her.

Then followed an amazing strange voyage, and Barnaby could not tell whether it was of three or ten days' duration. They lived in the circumstances of a nightmare, yet were very happy together.

The brigantine in which they sailed was manned by the strangest crew, who paid no attention whatever to Barnaby and the young lady. Only the captain of this outlandish crew might sometimes speak a few words to Barnaby, but otherwise he and Marjorie were left to themselves.

At first Marjorie was very quiet, but eventually her face grew bright and she smiled often as Barnaby talked with her and looked into her eyes. Neither kept track of the passing days, and Barnaby was surprised indeed when he came on deck one morning to find their ship lying alongside Staten Island in New York Harbor. Whether or not he wished to escape, he could see that he and the young lady were so closely watched they might have been prisoners.

All day there was much mysterious coming and going aboard the brigantine, and the captain was carried up to town in a sailboat that held a great load covered with a tarpaulin. Just as the sun was dropping below the water the captain came aboard once more and bade Barnaby come into the saloon, where Miss Marjorie was sitting.

The captain said to Barnaby, "You may think me the captain of this brigantine, but I am not. I have only carried out the orders of a superior in all I have done." He said that one more thing remained for him to do, the greatest of all. Barnaby and the young lady had not been fetched from the *Belle Helen* by chance but according to a plan of one wiser than he—one whom he must obey in all things. He hoped that Barnaby and the young lady would perform willingly what they now would be called upon to do, but willingly or not they must obey the orders.

Barnaby held his breath, not knowing what to expect. How great was his joy when the captain said that he had been ordered to take Barnaby and the young lady ashore and see them married. He already had arranged with a minister in the nearby shore village. "Such are my orders, and this is the last thing I am set to do."

The man left Barnaby and Marjorie to talk the matter over. Barnaby once more declared his great love for Marjorie, but said if she were unwilling to marry him he would rather die than have her forced to do so. With shining eyes, Marjorie told him she loved him and wanted to marry him.

Presently the captain returned, and, on seeing that all was settled happily, he wished them both joy. The yawl belonging to the brigantine was ready, and they sailed ashore. The captain and two other men of the brigantine walked after them up the village street to the minister's house.

After the wedding the same sailboat that had taken the captain to town in the afternoon was waiting for them. The captain wished them Godspeed, and Marjorie and Barnaby pushed off in it. Coming about they ran with the slant of the wind, leaving the shore and those strange beings behind them in the night.

As they sped through the darkness they heard the creaking of sails being hoisted aboard the brigantine and knew she was about to put to sea once more. Neither Barnaby True nor anyone else ever set eyes upon those beings again.

It was nigh midnight when Barnaby and Marjorie made Mr. Hartright's wharf at the foot of Wall Street, and the streets were dark and silent as they walked up to Barnaby's home. When Barnaby's stepfather was awakened and unlocked the door to see Barnaby and the beautiful young lady, he thought the *Belle Helen* had come to port. Barnaby waited until they were inside where no one could hear before telling his strange, wonderful story.

His amazed stepfather then led him into the dining room and held up a lighted candle so Barnaby could see a chest that had been left that afternoon for him by two foreign sailors. Barnaby, astonished, cried, "It is one of the two treasure chests Sir John fetched from Jamaica and which the pirates took from the *Belle Helen*."

Two days later the *Belle Helen* came to port with the terrible news of having been attacked at night by pirates. Also, Sir John Malyoe was dead. Whether it was the shock of seeing the face of Captain Brand, whom he had murdered, flashing out in the darkness, or whether it was the strain and excitement, certain it was that when the pirates left the *Belle Helen,* carrying with them the young lady and Barnaby, Sir John Malyoe lay in a fit on the floor and died the next morning without having spoken one word.

Nobody ever saw the manservant again. Whether he jumped overboard or whether the pirates carried him off, who shall say?

Mr. Hartright, after hearing Barnaby's story, had been uncertain as to the ownership of the chest, but Sir John's death made the matter easy to decide. Surely if the treasure did not belong to Barnaby, it must belong to his wife, who was Sir John's heir. So the fortune came to Barnaby True, grandson of that famous pirate, Willian Brand. The English estate in Devonshire descended to the Captain Malyoe whom Marjorie was to have married.

Whether that strange appearance of Captain Brand's face by the light of the pistol was a ghostly and spiritual appearance or whether he was present in flesh and blood, there is only this to say— he never was heard of again; nor had he ever been heard of till that time, since the day he was shot from behind by Captain John Malyoe on the banks of the Rio Cobra River in the year 1733.

—adapted by MILDRED CORELL LUCKHARDT
from *Howard Pyle's Book of Pirates*.

Halloween—Spooky but Fun!

Halloween is a scary, spooky night, but fun, too. Varieties of many of its customs are a couple of thousand years old. To try to tell exactly where many Halloween customs began is difficult because often folktales, superstitions, and customs have been carried from place to place.

Long ago when Druids were powerful among Celtic people on the British Isles and in what is now France, they worshiped the sun. They thought that when the sun died or was captured at the end of October the powers of darkness, death and evil took control. Most people knew little of science or the progress of the seasons. They mourned the death of the sun and thought that for the next six months it was busy fighting enemies who were in league with the evil Lord of Darkness and Death, Samhain.

The Druids' chief god was Baal or Bel, and his symbol was the sun. But nobody knows how the idea of Baal came to the Celts, for he was a very ancient god in the nature religions of Babylonia and the Near East. By various names the sun god was worshiped in many lands.

In Egypt thousands of years ago the sun god was called Ra, and his symbol was the sun disk. Egyptian myths tell that Osiris, also known as "God of the Sun," was slain by his brother Set, god of darkness and evil. On the anniversary each year of Osiris' death, the Egyptians were afraid to begin any new business because the spirit of evil and darkness was in power and would bring them bad luck. The Egyptians thought a great deal about death and life after death. They had many gods, ceremonies, and sacred animals, including the sacred cat.

The Druids also thought much about death and Samhain, Lord of Death. Samhain was associated not only with the sun's death but with death in general. For the Druids the year ended on October 31, for then all nature seemed to be dying. Leaves withered and fell, plants drooped, farms yielded no more crops. Cold weather came, and sickness, and frightening, evil creatures and happenings.

They thought that in October, on this last night of the old year, Samhain, Lord of Darkness and Death, gathered the souls or spirits of those who had died during the past year. Some folks thought that all spirits of the dead of the past year had lived in animals until that night. Those who had been wicked had been condemned to live in the bodies of cruel or loathesome animals. Then, on that night at October's end, the spirits gathered and Samhain decided what forms they should take for the next year.

Naturally, people did not want to be outdoors when these ghostly souls came hurrying from far and wide. Ghosts in animal skins and ghosts that floated through the air at Samhain's call were very scary. Too, it was thought that witches and demons often were abroad that night to help Samhain. In order not to be recognized, people sometimes disguised themselves—just in case some ghost wanted to pay off an old grudge or a witch wanted to cast a spell. Perhaps in those long-ago times some people streaked themselves with homemade dyes or bits of chalk to aid their disguise, and from that may have come the custom that still exists in some places where on Halloween children chalk one another's coats. It may be, too, that wearing one's coat inside out on Halloween originated in the same fashion for wearing clothes inside out was thought to guard against witches and other magical creatures. Or, perhaps, children began this custom so that the outsides of their coats would not be marked with Halloween chalk.

To the Druids also the cat was sacred. In time, black cats became connected with Halloween, perhaps because they were thought to have mystical powers. Cats often were thought to be helpers of witches or the devil. Sometimes they were feared as having been changed from human beings by evil magic. In some places the cat was thought to be the corn-spirit that must be caught at harvest time.

Into the Celtic harvest festivals long ago came many of these ideas. Druid priests in long white robes usually met the people by a stone altar on a hilltop in an oak forest, or close to an oak tree, for oaks were sacred to them. Some thought the god of fire lived in the oak for it was possible to make sparks quickly by rubbing dry oak twigs together.

At the Celtic October festival Druids thanked the sun god for their good harvest and promised to help him in his fight against the evil spirits of darkness, cold, and death. Since evil spirits fear light and fire, and fire is bright and warm like the sun, the Druids lit a new sacred fire for the new season. These fires for the Samhain or Bel festival could be seen on many hilltops as people celebrated.

To honor the god, animals were thrown into the fires. Sometimes the Celts, as did people of other lands, sacrificed to the god criminals or prisoners of war, burning them alive in wicker cages. There were many cruel rites performed by Druid priests at this Samhain festival. The entire festival, including the hilltop fires, was meant to please the god and persuade him to protect the people and their herds and crops. Besides that, the fire would frighten away evil spirits.

Like many pagan priests, Druid priests were believed to foresee the future. So, on Samhain Eve, with the help of spirits, they foretold what would happen during the new year. This was a time of mystery, fear, fortune-telling, and dread of the future. There was feasting, too, and parading around in costumes of animal skins and masks of animal heads. This was to keep away evil spirits and please Samhain.

First this October festival honored the sun for giving the harvest and encouraged him in his winter-long fight to get back to earth. After midnight the festival honored Samhain, the Lord of Darkness and Death, who brought winter. At the end of the feast each family carried home a torch lighted from the sacred fire. With this, the head of the house rekindled the home fire, which had been allowed to die just before the festival began. Since these torchlights scared away evil spirits who lurked close by, the people dashed down the hill, each trying not to be last. They thought the devil might "take the hindmost."

At the same time of year, about November 1, the ancient Romans celebrated harvest festivals, also. When apples and nuts were ripe, they honored Pomona, the goddess of fruit trees and orchards, and they thanked her for the harvest. Games and races were enjoyed, nuts were roasted, and baskets of apples were shared.

After many years the Romans conquered and ruled Britain, and those who went there to live took a number of holiday customs with them; but, although Romans had banished Druids, many Samhain customs persisted in Britain. In time they mingled with Pomona celebration in one big fall festival. Bonfires blazed as of old, and afterward people gathered around their home fires and scared themselves with tales of ghostly happenings and of evil spirits and witches.

As years passed, the ancient Roman religion dwindled. Former festivals at the change of seasons came to have new meaning and new names as they were conducted by the church. In the ninth century a pope set aside a day in May for ceremonies and prayers for all saints who had died. This day brought such crowds of people to Rome that the date was moved to November 1 when there would be enough food from the harvest to feed them. So November 1 became All Saints' or All Hallows' Day, with the preceding day and evening being All Hallows' Eve. Later November 2 became All Souls' Day. In early Anglo-Saxon days, hallow was the word for saint or holy.

Bonfires blazed in many places on these holy days to light souls to heaven and to scare away the Devil and evil spirits in league with the Devil. Torchlights were carried, too, for the same reason. These were times of mystery and of fear of death and the unknown. Also, they were days to remember people who had lived good lives and gone to Paradise. Besides solemn thoughts and rituals, everyone enjoyed merry-making and feasting to celebrate the harvest.

If any Celt was brave enough to go out on the Eve of All Hallows', or Halloween as it came to be called, he carried a light. Some lights were carried in big carved-out turnips, plentiful at harvesttime. Some were in pumpkins, also plentiful. These Halloween lights were called jack-o'-lanterns because, according to an old Irish tale, a mean and stingy man named Jack was sent after he died to the Devil. The Devil didn't want Jack, so he gave him a burning coal from hell's fire and told him to put it into the turnip on which he was chewing and move elsewhere with his turnip lantern. So Jack-o'-lantern still wanders about on the night when spirits are abroad, looking for a place to stay.

Lights carried on Halloween were a reminder, too, of bonfires that had blazed on the hills for Samhain. These lights could cheer the ghosts of the dead who were welcomed home for that night; also they could scare away unfriendly ghosts. And light always was thought to drive away witches who might want to harm travelers or enter homes. On Halloween wicked old women were said to become witches and fly off to meet the Devil in a wild gathering at which were many imps of Satan and bogies and goblins. Sometimes Halloween lights were called "bogies."

Nobody wanted to meet a witch, especially after she had sniffed her "flying ointment," which was made up of drugs that sent her off on a "trip." Often these "witches" who were on a drug trip did dangerous things. Sometimes, they did not even remember later what they had done when they were dashing through the neighborhood to meet others who were drugged. But lights usually scared them off.

Naturally, sometimes young people liked to pretend to be ghosts or witches or goblins or the Devil. They would dress up in costumes and scare travelers or creep up on farmhouses and make weird noises, peer in at the doors, and disappear.

Halloween never became a religious festival of the church, but it became a time for fun and masquerading, as well as being scary. Countryfolk, especially in Ireland, enjoyed going from farmhouse to farmhouse begging for food then, because many farmers had stored away a good harvest. The leader of the begging parade wore a white robe like that of the ancient Druids and a mask like a horse head. This custom probably came from the wearing of animal heads centuries before at Samhain festivals. Often they begged in the name of Muck Olla, an ancient Druid god, and said that if the farmer and his wife gave them treats of food Muck Olla would bring good luck to their farm. If they got no treats they might play mean tricks.

In England, Halloween often was called Snap Apple Night or Nutcrack Night. Instead of venturing far, nearby neighbors often gathered in one home and roasted newly harvested nuts and apples and told fortunes from the way nuts cracked or from apple peelings. Since from ancient times this had been a night of fortune-telling, young people wanted to know when and whom they would marry. Apples and nuts were used in various ways to tell fortunes. In some places in the British Isles apples were floated in a pan of water, and people bobbed for them. The first person to get an apple in his teeth would be the first to marry.

Mirrors always have been connected with fortune-telling, especially at Halloween. A girl looked in a mirror to see what young man's face would be reflected there, for he was the one she would marry. A young man might see his future wife while he sowed hempseed and spoke an old rhyme about it. Sometimes "fortunes" were hidden in Halloween cakes or other food.

Begging from house to house sometimes was done on All Souls' Day instead of Halloween, and was called "going a-souling." The "soulers," in return for treats, promised to say special prayers for the souls of the dead. Often they were given cakes called "soul cakes." If not given a soul cake or other treat, they might do mean tricks such as angry ghosts were thought to do if not well treated.

After many years, only groups of children went begging from

house to house and were given treats of nuts, apples, sweets, or coins. Sometimes they stood outside a house door and began singing a chant that started "Soul, soul, an apple or two." They kept on singing, naming various treats they would accept, and ended "Give us good alms, and we'll be gone." Most of this was in fun, but they usually were given treats so they would not destroy something or cause trouble.

In some ways the soul cake was used as a bribe or sop to pacify the soulers. Nobody knows just when or where the idea of the soul cake started. One ancient Greek myth tells of Cerberus, a dog that guarded the entrance to the Lower Region. Pluto, Lord of Darkness, ruled this Lower Region of Departed Souls, sometimes called Hades. Pluto was thought of not as a devil but as a strict ruler who kept order there and controlled a vast store of treasure hidden. Cerberus was such a fierce watchdog that souls had a hard time getting past him. So it was the custom for people to put a soul cake into the hand of a person who had just died, and Cerberus would take the cake as a bribe or sop and let the soul go through.

In many places, including Eastern Wales, the eve of All Souls' Day is a time for giving generous gifts to the poor. The idea of giving on Halloween to those in need has entered into celebrations everywhere. The gifts are collected in different ways in different countries. In the United States every Halloween, thousands of girls and boys go begging for money for UNICEF, so that children all over the world may receive needed food, milk, and medicine. This kind of Halloween begging began with a Sunday school class in 1950 and soon spread throughout the whole country! Now generous people everywhere are glad to give money to buy treats for the world's children.

And in countless villages, towns, and cities, children who have come from many different countries throughout the world gather on the main streets days before Halloween to paint pictures on store windows. Witches, ghosts, goblins, devils, and jack-o'-lanterns soon peer from the window paintings at all the people who wander in groups up and down the streets to enjoy the pictures the young artists have made.

Then as Halloween draws nearer many of these same children get costumes and masks together to wear on the spooky night. Often they take the costumes to school beforehand and have a costume parade, with the older girls and boys helping the little ones. Often older children and grown-ups give Halloween parties at hospitals for the children who cannot go out for trick or treat.

For days before Halloween a spirit of fun is stirring. Halloween night is fun and spooky, when girls and boys in all sorts of costumes roam through the dark while one of the big ones carries a jack-o'-lantern. It is a night of fun and parties, pranks and mischief, of apples, nuts, fortune-telling, and sharing with others.

Sometimes when a group of young spooks has left a house with their bags of treats or UNICEF boxes, they go off into the night following a jack-o'-lantern and singing:

> Jack-o'-lantern, trim your light,
> Fairies come and dance tonight:
> Skipping, tripping on the Green,
> Merry be your Halloween!

—MILDRED CORELL LUCKHARDT

Halloween

Tonight is the night
When dead leaves fly
Like witches or switches
Across the sky,
When elf and sprite
Flit through the night
On a moony sheen.

Tonight is the night
When leaves make a sound
Like a gnome in his home
Under the ground,

When spooks and trolls
Creep out of holes
Mossy and green.

Tonight is the night
When pumpkins stare
Through sheaves and leaves
Everywhere,
When ghoul and ghost
And goblin host
Dance round their queen
It's Halloween.

—HARRY BEHN

Finn Mac Cool and
the Stranger of the Flaming Breath

In the proud, far back days of Erin there arose a mighty brother-hood called the Fianna. They were a war-host whose task was to hold the shores of Erin from invaders, and they were a peace-host, for it was their task also to keep down raids and harryings and blood feuds between the five lesser kingdoms into which Erin was divided. They each had a Fianna company and Fian Chief; but one Captain was over all and every man must take his oath of loyalty to the Captain and the High King of Erin. The High King sat in his high hall at Tara with his right foot upon the Stone of Destiny.

When Cool Mac Trenmor, Lord of the Clan Bascna, was Captain of all the Fianna, Aed Mac Morna, Lord of the Clan Morna and Chief of the Connacht Fianna, sought the Captaincy for himself. At Cnucha, near where Dublin stands today, a great battle was fought in which one of Cool's household warriors wounded Aed in the eye, so sorely that he went by the name of Goll, which means one-eyed, after that.

181

Then Goll Mac Morna dealt Cool Mac Trenmor a death blow, and he took from Cool's belt a certain bag of blue- and crimson-dyed crane-skin that was the Treasure Bag of the Fianna. And with the death of Cool and loss of the Treasure Bag, the battle went against Clan Bascna and those who were left of the Leinster Fianna as well as the Munster men who had stood with them were driven into the Connacht hills.

News of the battle and of Cool's death was brought to his young wife Murna and she near her time to bear his child. And Murna, knowing that her lord's enemies would not allow any child of his to live, fled, taking two of her most trusted women with her, into the wild fastnesses of Slieve Bloom. There she bore a manchild, and not daring to keep him with her for fear of the hunters on her trail, she gave him to the two women, bidding them bring him up in the hidden glens until he was of an age to fight for his rightful place as Cool's son. Then, sadly, she went her way alone.

In the hidden glens of Slieve Bloom, the boy grew up and the women trained him in all the ways of the wild. By the time he was a youth he was such a hunter that he could run down the deer on his naked feet without even a hound to help him; and he knew the ways of wolf and otter, badger and fox and falcon.

As he grew older he began to range far and wide. One day he came to the hall of a great chieftain before which some boys were playing hurley. After they gave him a hurley stick and told him the rules he soon could play better and swifter than any of them. When the boys told the chieftain of the strange boy whose name they did not know, they said "He is tall and strong and the hair of him as bright as barley when it whitens in the sun at harvest time."

The chieftain named him Finn, which means fair. Later, the chieftain spoke of him to a friend on the hunting trail, and the friend spoke to another, and as time went by rumors of Finn's skill and daring spread until they came to the ears of Goll Mac Morna. It seemed to Goll that if Cool had a son he would be just such a one as Finn. The boy would be fourteen now. Goll mustered the Connacht Fianna and bade them hunt the boy down and bring him back, living or dead. Goll knew that Finn, not he, was the rightful Captain of the Fianna of Erin.

But one of Finn's foster-mothers warned him. So Finn took his sling, his warmest cloak and a spear and set out on his wanderings. He took service with now this king or chieftain and now that, getting weapon-skill and warrior training, against the day when he should stand out in the open and fight for his rightful place in the world.

He began to gather to him a band of young men and in time led them into Connacht to seek any of his father's old followers who might yet be living in the hills. The day after they crossed the border Finn met a woman stricken with grief because her son had been slain by Lia of Luachair. Finn fought Lia and slew him. And when Lia lay dead, Finn saw the strange-seeming crane-skin bag, blue and crimson, fastened to his belt.

Taking the bag with him, he later came upon the aging remnants of Clan Bascna. Among them were his father's brother, who, at sight of the bag cried, "The Treasure Bag of the Fianna!" Goll Mac Morna had taken it from Cool's body. "With it will return the lordship of the Fianna. Take your father's place, Finn Mac Cool."

Finn left the Treasure Bag with his uncle and set off alone once more, to learn from a Druid who lived on the banks of the Boyne. He knew that before he was fitted to take his father's place he must study poetry and the tales in which lay the ancient wisdom and history of his people. After seven years studying and serving the Druid,

Finn received mystical knowledge and power and was ready to go forth alone once more.

Now, when he left his Druid master beside the Boyne, Finn knew that the time was come for him to be claiming his father's place, and he set out for Tara of the High Kings.

It was Samhein, the time of the great autumn feast, and as he drew nearer, his road, and the four other roads that met at Tara, became more and more densely thronged with chiefs and warriors, on horseback or in chariots decorated with bronze and walrus ivory, with their women in gowns of green and saffron and crimson and heather-dark plaid and the golden apples swinging from the ends of their braided hair, and their tall feather-heeled hounds running alongside. For at Samhein all the kings and chiefs of Erin came together, and all men were free to sit at table in the High King's hall if they could find room—and so long as they left weapons outside.

So up the Royal Hill and in through the gate, and across the broad forecourt went Finn, amid the incoming throng, and sat himself down with the King's household warriors, ate badger's meat baked with salt and honey, and drank the yellow mead from a silver-bound oxhorn, and watched the High King and the tall scarred man close beside him, who he knew from his lack of an eye must be Goll Mac Morna, and waited for the King to notice that there was a stranger among his warriors.

And presently the High King did notice him, and sent one of his court officials to bid him come and stand before the High Table.

"What is your name? And why do you come and seat yourself unannounced among my household warriors?" demanded the King.

And Finn flung up his pale bright head and gave him back stare for stare. "I am Finn the son of Cool who was once Captain of all the Fianna of Erin, Cormac High King, and I am come to carry my spear in your service as he did; but for me, I will carry it in the ranks of your household warriors, and not with the Fianna." This he said because he knew that to join the Fianna he would have to swear faith to Goll Mac Morna, and he was no light faith-breaker.

"If you are the son of Cool, then you may be proud of your birth," said the King. "Your father was a mighty hero, and his speer I trusted as I would trust my own—and as I will trust yours."

Then Finn swore faith to Cormac the High King; and Cormac gave him a place among his household warriors, and the feasting went on as it had done before, and the King's harper beat upon his curved harp while the mead horns passed from hand to hand, and the great hounds fought over the bones among the rushes on the floor.

But little by little the drink began to pass more slowly, the laughter grew fitful and the harp-song fell away, and men began to half glance into each other's eyes and break off the glance quickly, as though afraid of what they might see.

And indeed they had good reason.

Every Samhein for the past twenty years, Tara had been weirdly and terribly visited. Fiend or Fairy, no one knew what the strange-comer was, only that his name was Aillen of the Flaming Breath, and that every Samhein at midnight he came upon them from the Fairy hill close by and burned the royal dun (this fortress of Tara) over their heads.

No use for any warrior, however valiant, to try to withstand him, for he carried a silver harp, and as he came he drew from the strings the sweetest and most drowsy music that ever breathed upon the ears of men, and all who heard it drifted into enchanted sleep.

So each Samhein it was the same; he came upon Tara with no one left awake to withstand him, and he breathed where he would with a licking breath of fire until thatch and timber blackened and scorched and twisted, and kindled into leaping flame. So every year Tara must be rebuilt, and every year again—and yet again.

When the sounds of feasting had died quite away, and an uneasy hush with little stirrings and little eddies in it held the King's hall, Cormac rose in his High Place, and offered a mighty reward in gold and horses and women slaves to any warrior who could prevail against Aillen of the Flaming Breath, and keep the thatch on Tara till the next day's dawn.

He made the same offer, and his father before him, twenty Samhein nights, and after the first few times, no man, not the boldest of his warriors, had come forward in answer, for they knew that neither courage nor skill nor strength would avail them against the wicked silvery music. So Cormac made the offer, and waited, without hope.

And then Finn rose in his place, and stood to face the troubled King. "Cormac Mac Art, High King of Erin, I will forgo the gold and the horses and the women slaves, but if I prevail this horror of the night, and keep the thatch on Tara till tomorrow's dawn, will you swear before all these in your hall to give me my rightful heritage?"

"It is a bold man, I'm thinking, who seeks to bargain with the High King," said Cormac. "What heritage is that?"

"The Captaincy of the Fianna of Erin."

"I have given you the place that you asked for among my own warriors," said Cormac, "and is that not good enough for you?"

"Not if I keep the thatch on Tara," said Finn.

Then a murmur ran round the hall, and men looked at each other and at Goll Mac Morna, who sat looking straight before him with his one bright falcon's eye.

"I swear," said the King, "and let all those gathered here, the kings and chiefs of Erin, warriors of my household and of all the Fianna, witness to my swearing. If you overcome Aillen of the Flaming Breath, you will have earned the Captaincy in your own right, and in your own right as well as by heritage, you shall hold it."

So Finn left the King's hall, and took up his spear that he had laid by when he entered, and went up to the rampart walk that crested the encircling turf wall. He did not know at all how he should succeed when so many had failed before him, but his faith was in his destiny, and he did not doubt that he would prevail. And while he paced to and fro, waiting and watching, and listening more than all, one of the older warriors came after him, carrying a spear with its head laced into a leather sheath.

"Long ago your father saved my life," said the man, "and now is the time to be repaying my debt. Take the spear, to aid you in your fight."

"I have a good spear of my own," Finn said.

But the other shook his head. "Not such a spear as this, that must be kept hooded like a hawk lest it run wild and drink blood of its own accord. It was forged by Lein, the Smith of the Gods, and he beat into it the fire of the sun and the potency of the moon. When you hear the first breath of the fairy music, lay the blade to your forehead, and the fierceness and the bloodlust in it will drive away all sleep from you. Take it."

Finn took the spear and loosed the thongs and slipped off the cover. He saw a spearhead of iron as sheeny-blue as the moonlight, and studded with thirty rivets of bright Arabian gold.

"Take it," said the man once more.

And Finn hooded the spear again, but left the thongs loose. And carrying it, he returned to his pacing up and down, looking always

out over the plains of Mide, white under the moon, and listening, listening until the silence in his own ears sounded loud as the hushing of the sea in a shell.

And then it came, the faintest gossamer shimmer of distant harpmusic. Nearer and clearer, even as he checked to listen, clearer and nearer; the fairy music lapped like the first gentle wavelets of sleep about him. It was the light summer wind through the moorland grasses of Slieve Bloom, it was the murmur of bees among the sunwarmed bell heather; it was all the lullabies that ever his foster mothers had sung to him when he was too young to remember.

Finn tore himself free of the enchantment that was weaving itself around him, and with fingers that seemed weak and numb, dragged the leather hood from the spear and pressed the blade to his forehead. Instantly he heard the voice of the spear more clearly than Aillen's harp; an angry hornet note that drove all sleep away from him. His head cleared, and looking out once more toward the Fairy hill, he saw a thing like a mist-wraith floating toward him along the ground.

Nearer and nearer, taking shape and substance as it came, until Finn was looking at the pale airy shape of Aillen of the Flaming

Breath, so near and clear now that he could even catch the silver ripple of the harpstrings on which the thing played with long white fingers as he came. Now Aillen had reached the stockade which crowned the turf walls, and a long tongue of greenish flame shot from his mouth and lapped at the timbers.

Finn tore off his mantle of saffron-eyed ram skins, and with one sweep of it, beat the flame into the ground.

With his flame beaten out, Aillen gave a terrible wailing cry, and turned over and back, streaming through himself like a wave flung back by a rocky shore, and fled away toward the Fairy hill. But Finn, with the hornet-shouting of the spear loud and urgent in his ears, leapt the stockade and was after him, as swift as he.

The doorway of the Fairy hill stood open, letting out a green twilight, and as Aillen fled wailing toward it, Finn made one mighty cast with the spear, and the spear flew on its way rejoicing, and passed through the creature's body and out at the other side. And there on the threshold of the Fairy hill—or where the threshold had been, for now the door was gone, and only the frost-crisped grass and bramble gleamed faintly under the moon—Aillen of the Flaming Breath lay dead, like a heap of thistledown and touchwood and the fungus that grows on the north side of trees, tangled together into somewhat the shape of a man.

Then Finn cut off the head and set it on the point of his spear and carried it back to Tara and set it up on the walls for all to see.

When morning came, and Tara still stood as it had stood last night, all men knew that Finn must have prevailed against Aillen of the Flaming Breath, and led by the High King they went out to the ramparts; and there they found Finn leaning wearily on the stockade and waiting for their coming, and nothing to show for the happenings of the night but the scorch marks on his saffron cloak which he had wrapped close about himself against the dawn chill, and the strange and ghastly head upreared on his spear point against the morning sky.

"I have kept the thatch on Tara," Finn said.

Then Cormac Mac Art set his arm across the young man's shoulders, and turned with him to face the mighty gathering in the forecourt below. "Chiefs and kings and warriors, last night ye bore witness when I swore in the mead hall that if this Finn son of Cool should prevail against Aillen of the Flaming Breath, I would set him in his father's place as Captain of the Fianna of Erin. Last night it was in my mind that it was small chance he had, where so many had failed before. But he has prevailed; he has slain the fire fiend and saved Tara, and therefore I give him to you of the Fianna for your Captain, according to my word and yours. Any of you that will not serve under him, let you leave Erin, freely and without disgrace; there are other war bands and kings' bodyguards overseas in other lands."

He turned to the tall one-eyed man who stood out before the rest. "That is for you also, Goll Mac Morna, for you who have been the Fian Captain these eighteen years past. Will you strike hands with Finn Mac Cool, and lead the Connacht Fianna under him? Or will you cross the sea and carry your sword into the services of another king?"

"I will strike hands with Finn the son of Cool my old enemy," said Goll Mac Morna, though the words stuck a little in his throat, and he and Finn spat in the palms and struck hands like two men sealing a bargain.

No man went out from the High King's forecourt to carry his

sword overseas, and the feud between Clan Morna and Clan Bascna, though it was not healed, was skinned over and remained so for many years to come.

So Finn Mac Cool became Captain of the Fianna of Erin, as his father had been before him.

—From *The High Deeds of Finn Mac Cool* BY ROSEMARY SUTCLIFF

Tamlane

"The night it is good Hallowe'en,
   When fairy folk will ride;
And they that wad their true love win
   At Miles Cross they maun bide."

These words were spoken by an Elfin knight named Tamlane to beautiful Janet who had dared to come alone to Carterhaugh Wood where it was said that Tamlane wove his spells. The story of young Tamlane and Janet was first told hundreds of years ago by minstrels who wandered from castle to castle and cottage to cottage, singing their stories as ballads. The ballad of the young Tamlane has been sung or spoken and acted in many places for years, especially on Halloween, when magic folk are said to gather and the Devil has great power. Beginning on the next page is the story, retold in prose by Joseph Jacobs in More English Fairy Tales, *published by G. P. Putnam's Sons.*

192

Tamlane

Young Tamlane was son of Earl Murray, and Burd Janet was daughter of Dunbar, Earl of March. And when they were young they loved each other and plighted their troth. But when the time came near for marrying, Tamlane disappeared, and none knew what had become of him.

Many, many days after he had disappeared, Burd Janet was wandering in Carterhaugh Wood, though she had been warned not to go there. And as she wandered she plucked the flowers from the bushes. She came at last to a bush of broom and began plucking it. She had not taken more than three flowerets when by her side up started young Tamlane.

"Where come ye from, Tamlane, Tamlane?" Burd Janet said; "and why have you been away so long?"

"From Elfland I come," said young Tamlane. "The Queen of Elfland has made me her knight."

"But how did you get there, Tamlane?" said Burd Janet.

"I was hunting one day, and as I rode widdershins round yon hill, a deep drowsiness fell upon me, and when I awoke, behold! I was in Elfland. Fair is that land and gay, and fain would I stop but for thee and one other thing. Every seven years the Elves pay their tithe to the Nether world, and for all the Queen makes much of me, I fear it is myself that will be the tithe."

"Oh, can you not be saved? Tell me if aught I can do will save you, Tamlane?"

"Only one thing there is for my safety. Tomorrow night is Hallowe'en, and the fairy court will then ride through England and Scotland, and if you would borrow me from Elfland you must take your stand by Miles Cross between twelve and one o' the night, and with holy water in your hand you must cast a compass all around you."

"But how shall I know you, Tamlane?" quoth Burd Janet, "amid so many knights I've ne'er seen before?"

"The first court of Elves that come by let pass. The next court you shall pay reverence to, but do naught nor say aught. But the third court that comes by is the chief court of them, and at the head rides the Queen of all Elfland. And I shall ride by her side upon a milk-white steed with a star in my crown; they give me this honour as being a christened knight. Watch my hands, Janet, the right one will be gloved but the left one will be bare, and by that token you will know me."

"But how to save you, Tamlane?" quoth Burd Janet.

"You must spring upon me suddenly, and I will fall to the ground. Then seize me quick, and whatever change befall me, for they will exercise all their magic on me, cling hold to me till they turn me into red-hot iron. Then cast me into this pool and I will be turned back into a mother-naked man. Cast then your green mantle over me, and I shall be yours, and be of the world again."

So Burd Janet promised to do all for Tamlane, and next night at midnight she took her stand by Miles Cross and cast a compass round her with holy water.

Soon there came riding by the Elfin court, first over the mound went a troop of black steeds and then another troop of brown. But in the third court, all on milkwhite steeds, she saw the Queen of Elf-land, and by her side a knight with a star in his crown, with right hand gloved and the left bare. Then she knew this was her own Tamlane, and springing forward she seized the bridle of the milk-white stead and pulled its rider down. And as soon as he touched the ground she let go the bridle and seized him in her arms.

"He's won, he's won amongst us all," shrieked out the eldritch crew, and all came around her and tried their spells on young Tamlane.

First they turned him in Janet's arms like frozen ice, then into a huge flame of roaring fire. Then, again, the fire vanished and an adder was skipping through her arms, but still she held on; and then they turned him into a snake that reared up as if to bite her, and yet she held on. Then suddenly a dove was struggling in her arms, and almost flew away. Then they turned him into a swan, but all was in vain, till at last he turned into a red-hot glaive, and this she cast into a well of water and he turned back into a mother-naked man. She quickly cast her green mantle over him, and young Tamlane was Burd Janet's for ever.

Then sang the Queen of Elfland as the court turned away and began to resume its march:

> "She that has borrowed young Tamlane
>   Has gotten a stately groom,
> She's taken away my bonniest knight,
>   Left nothing in his room.
>
> "But had I known, Tamlane, Tamlane,
>   A lady would borrow thee,
> I'd hae ta'en out thy two gray eyne,
>   Put in two eyne of tree.
>
> "Had I but known, Tamlane, Tamlane,
>   Before we came from home,
> I'd hae ta'en out thy heart o' flesh,
>   Put in a heart of stone.

"Had I but had the wit yestreen
   That I have got to-day,
I'd paid the Fiend seven times his teind
   Ere you'd been won away."

And then the Elfin court rode away, and Burd Janet and young Tamlane went their way homeward and were soon after married after young Tamlane had again been sained by the holy water.

—JOSEPH JACOBS

Buy Me!

Pumpkin, pumpkin, buy a pumpkin!
See how big I am . . . and fat!
Want a jolly jack-o'-lantern?
Cut a face and add a hat!

Buy me for your jack-o'-lantern,
Pig-tailed girl with impish grin.
Look me over. Don't you like me?
See my color! Touch my skin!

I would like to be your pumpkin,
Red-haired boy with freckled nose.
Can't you tell that I'm the best one?
Buy me. Don't take one of those!

Don't choose me, not me, dear lady!
I can see it in your eye,
You are shopping for a pumpkin
You can bake into a pie!

197

All last summer in that cornfield,
There I slumbered in the sun,
Dreaming how on Halloween
I'd be having so much fun.

Can't you see that I'm too handsome?
Don't you know the reason why?
I'm a jack-o'-lantern pumpkin,
I just can't end up a pie!

Red-haired boy come back and save me!
She is looking at me, still.
Pick me quick or she'll decide to
Put me on her grocery bill!

You may think me patient, silent,
As I sit here in this row.
But I'm really shouting, SHOUTING!
Can't you hear me? Don't say no!

Now, you say, you've made your mind up?
And the one you want is me?
What a happy pumpkin I am!
What a night it's going to be!

—FRANCES LOWRY

Trina's Halloween Adventure

Trina Gonzales and her parents and big brother Jaime lived in a boxcar by the railroad tracks. Her father worked for the railroad, repairing tracks, and often the boxcar was hitched to an engine and the family was moved to another place. Jaime spoke both Spanish and English well, but Mama and Papa and Trina still spoke more Spanish than English. They never had lived long enough in one place for Trina to make friends, and she was shy about trying to speak English to strangers. Here in Wyoming as in many other places they had lived, only a few people spoke Spanish. The story that follows (from TRINA'S BOXCAR by Patricia M. Martin) tells of a Halloween adventure they all shared in Wyoming a number of years ago.

October came, and the boxcar was still in place on the siding. If only Papa could stay in this Wyoming town always. If—if only the engine would never hook on their boxcar and take them on to another place. Now the pastures were dry and brown. The tame ewe still came to the fence, and Trina pulled grass for her to eat.

The leaves on the little trees near the hotel turned brilliant yellow.

"It will soon be Halloween," Jaime said. "Pablo and Flavio and I are going out after dark and have fun.

"Mama," Trina said. "May I go with the boys and play tricks?"

"What do you mean, play tricks?" Mamma asked.

"We don't want her," Jaime said.

"What does she mean, play tricks?" Mama asked Jaime.

"Oh, nothing much. Maybe we knock on a door and hide. Things like that." Jaime stood first on one foot and then on another, and Trina knew that he wasn't telling everything.

"May I go, Mama?" she asked.

Papa spoke from his chair by the stove. "No. You may not. It is all right for boys to play their small, harmless tricks. Girls stay home."

"You can have a pumpkin lantern instead," Jaime said. "I'll help you make it."

Just before Halloween Jaime brought home a big pumpkin.

"Charlie Wilson's father got two in Cheyenne, and he gave one of them to me."

Their father sliced off the top, and Jaime and Trina scooped out the middle.

"The middle we will cook," Mama said. "Now."

With a pencil point Jaime scratched two eyes, and a nose and a laughing, toothy smile, and there was a pumpkin lantern with a fat, happy face.

"We need a candle to put inside," Jaime said.

"A little one," Trina said.

Mama opened the chest and lifted out her treasures. She set aside a small cardboard box and a cigar box.

"May I look in the cardboard box?" Trina asked.

It was a special treat to look in the cardboard box with its broken ends and its crumpled tissue paper. Trina knew what she would find there: a big gold heart that had been her mother's when mother was a little girl. Trina loved the heart. She looked inside and lifted the heart. She put a fingernail in the small crescent at the side, and the heart swung open on golden hinges. There was a picture inside.

It was funny and old-fashioned, but Trina loved it. There were three people in the picture: Grandfather and Grandmother in Mexico, young and different from the way Trina remembered them, with her mother, very small and smiling, standing at their knees.

Trina closed the locket and set it in its frame of tissue and put the lid on the box.

Mama lifted the cover of the cigar box. Inside were the ends of candles that had burned low. "I have exactly what you need," she said. "Here."

Jaime dug out a small place in the bottom of the pumpkin and set the candle inside.

"Now it's ready," Trina said.

After supper on Halloween Jaime pulled on his heavy jacket.

"Don't stay out late," Mama said. "I do not like this custom of going out after dark and playing tricks on our neighbors."

"But we cannot take from this country only those things we like best," Papa said. "We will learn to enjoy all its customs."

The pumpkin lantern was still burning when Jaime came back. He tossed his cap on a chair and wriggled out of his jacket.

"What did you do?" Trina asked. "Where did you go?"

"Oh, we knocked on the superintendent's window and scared

Maggie and Mrs. Tolley. And we took Mr. Green's sign and hung it upside down."

"If Mr. Green comes here in the morning and asks that you replace it, right side up, I will not object," said Papa.

"Who went with you?" Trina asked.

"Flavio and Ricardo and Pablo, and Charlie Wilson, and the other boys."

"And what else did you do, Jaime?" Papa asked.

"Oh, we turned over the old bench on the hotel porch. But we didn't hurt it any. Just things like that."

It was obvious that Jaime wanted to change the subject. He was worried for fear Papa would ask too many questions, but Papa didn't.

"Time for bed," Mama said in English. "Blow out the pumpkin."

"Blow out the *candle,* you mean, Mama," Jaime said.

Trina took a long time getting ready for bed. She undressed her doll Ana Maria and put her in the bunk in her petticoat. Then she got ready for bed herself and whispered her prayers.

Before breakfast next morning, there was a loud knocking at the door. Trina's father slid it open.

Mr. Wilson was outside, and anyone could tell he was angry.

"Mr. Gonzales," Mr. Wilson said. "Last night some of the boys around town put my young bull in the hayloft, and I know Jaime was with them. I want you and Jaime to come and help get it down."

"JAIME," Mr. Gonzales thundered. "DID YOU PUT THE BULL IN THE HAYLOFT?"

"No, sir." Jaime's voice sounded small and squeaky. Like a scared mouse, Trina thought. "I didn't go near that . . ."

Mr. Wilson interrupted. "Jaime, were you with Pablo and Ricardo and the rest of those boys who went around hanging signs upside down and turning over hotel benches?"

"Yes sir, but . . ."

"I saw all of you going by the stables on the way to the barn." Mr. Wilson was shouting.

"Charlie was with us," Jaime answered. "Charlie will tell you that we didn't even . . ."

"I know my Charlie was with that gang," Mr. Wilson said. "I'm not excusing him. Charlie will help get that bull down. Now I want you both to come along with me. We've got to figure some way to get that bull down before he hurts himself."

"We'll go," Jaime's father said. He gave Jaime a push between the shoulder blades. "Go."

Mr. Wilson led the way, and Mr. Gonzales followed with a grip on Jaime's arm. Jaime hopped along, one shoulder higher than the other.

Trina followed a distance behind them. She hoped that her father would not turn around and send her home. She would like to see everything and hear everything that was said. Jaime was in real trouble.

Mr. Marshall and Abner had already arrived. Abner had his box camera and was taking a picture of the bull in the hayloft door. Mr. Green was there too, and Charlie Wilson was kicking at the side of the barn.

The other fathers from the boxcars came with Pablo, Ricardo, and Flavio.

All the fathers were talking.

Mr. Green was on one knee beside a large coil of rope.

"As I see it," he said, "we have to make a harness strong enough to get that bull down." He looked at Mr. Wilson and nodded toward the door of the loft. "Is that pulley up there strong enough to hold a bull?"

"It's strong enough to hold this young bull," Mr. Wilson said. "What I'd like to know is how these boys got him up there." He turned to Charlie. "Did you use a rope and that pulley?"

Charlie shrugged his shoulders.

Mr. Green uncoiled the rope. "If we lay the rope like this—and tie it in place . . ."

They were weaving a harness—a place here for the bull's head, a place there for its legs, loose around the neck.

And then they were all going inside.

Papa suddenly became aware of Trina. *"Trina,* what are you doing here?"

"I want to see, Papa," Trina said. "I'll stay outside. I won't get in the way."

"Let her stay," said Mr. Wilson. "She can stay outside."

"Very well," Papa said. "Stand back out of the way."

Trina peeked through a crack between two boards.

They all were going up the big stairs that led steeply to the loft. Mr. Wilson was first.

There was scuffling and shouting in the loft, and Mr. Wilson's voice was louder than the rest.

"GOOD, WE'VE GOT HIM. EASY DOES IT. HANG ON. GET THE ROPE OVER THE PULLEY. HANG ON TIGHT. BRACE YOURSELF. SLIDE ALONG EASY. NOT SO FAST."

And the bull was coming down, suspended at the end of a rope, wound in its harness—slowly, slowly.

When it touched the ground, it scrambled about trying to free itself from the ropes. Mr. Wilson herded it into the barn.

Trina looked at the stern expression on her father's face. "He looks like a thundercloud," she thought. "There will be a big storm in our boxcar when we get home."

The parents and their sons started home. Trina stayed to take one more look at the bull.

"*Espéranse,* wait," she said. "*Ven ligerito,* come quick. *El toro,* the bull!"

The bull was climbing the stairs.

He disappeared into the hayloft.

Mr. Wilson scratched his ear. "Well, what do you think about that? He climbed those stairs by himself. You could knock me over with a feather."

"We will help you once more," Mr. Gonzales said. "We will help you get that bull down. Perhaps then you will be willing to tie him in his stall so this does not happen again?"

On their way home, Papa walked between Jaime and Trina. He put his hand on Jaime's shoulder.

Trina waited for Papa to speak.

"I hope you will excuse me," Papa said to Jaime. "Many times you will observe that parents are in the wrong." He nodded at Trina. "And you will also notice that mistakes are made as easily in English as in Spanish."

They walked on in silence. When they were crossing the tracks, Jaime spoke.

"Do you know what, Papa? Getting that bull out of the hayloft was more fun than Halloween."

Trina thought so, too.

—PATRICIA M. MARTIN

Theme in Yellow

I spot the hills
With yellow balls in autumn.
I light the prairie cornfields
Orange and tawny gold clusters
And I am called pumpkins.
On the last of October
When dusk is fallen
Children join hands
And circle round me
Singing ghost songs
And love to the harvest moon;
I am a jack-o'-lantern
With terrible teeth
And the children know
I am fooling.

—CARL SANDBURG

Halloween with Onion John

When Andy Rusch was twelve he and Eechee Ries, Bo Hemmendinger, and Bitsy Schwarz became friends of Onion John, a tall man who wore queer clothes, lived in a shack, and spent much time at the town dump. He knew many magic words and ceremonies and what magic to use to make rain. When the moon was right he cooked strange things into a stew to get gold from the moon.

The boys thought him a wizard, so they invited him to their Halloween party, which was to be in Andy's cellar this year. The four of them had a Halloween party and banquet each year, with a big cake decorated with their four last names. Onion John would be guest of honor and did not have to do any decorating or chip in to buy food.

After the party the boys were going with their fathers to the Rotary party where a magician would saw in half Mr. Kinnoy, the executive secretary.

The boys' Halloween parties were always fun, but didn't last very long even though they ate lots of food. This year, however, when the boys were ready to begin eating Onion John said they first must ward off witches and other evil creatures by fumigating the cellar. He sprinkled oil on dry leaves

208

in an old ash-barrel near the furnace. Then after Bitsy and Andy had made "living fire" with a wooden bow and stick, Onion John set the leaves afire, and smoke poured out.

Here is Andy's account of their Halloween party, from the book Onion John, *by Joseph Krumgold.*

Halloween with Onion John

It was the smoke we wanted, John explained. Any fiends around were knocked senseless by the smoke. And to make it rougher on them when they dropped, John had us turn all the chairs upside down with their feet sticking in the air. I found a lot of other stuff to mangle them with. We bumped around in the dark and stuck up a rake, an axe, a bag of old golf clubs and a crow bar. For witches, the cellar was worse than a booby trap. By then it was pretty bad on us, too, considering the smoke.

"Where's the door?" Bitsy started coughing. "Let me out of here!"

"For heaven's sakes!" It was my mother at the top of the stairs. "What goes on down there? Andy!"

The others headed for the basement door to the outside. I ran upstairs.

"Look at this kitchen," said my mother. It took me a little while, coming out of the dark, before I was able to look. Then I could see the big refrigerator and the stove all white and shining. And of course, a lot of smoke. And my father standing in the dining room door holding on to a magazine.

"Everything under control?" he asked.

"It's only a little fire in a barrel. It's almost out by now. We were fumigating for witches. With Onion John."

"John? Is he with you?"

It wasn't that I tried to keep it any secret from my father, the invitation. It never came up, any reason to mention it.

"I didn't know you ever had any older people," my mother said, "at your banquet."

"It's only Onion John's special," I explained, "when it comes to Halloween. There's a lot of history in what he knows. How Halloween started with souls eating. And why demons go flying around tonight. It's educational."

"And you're sure it's safe down there?" My mother flapped her apron at the smoke. "For everyone but witches."

"Well look, Andy," my father folded his magazine. "Suppose you hop down there and empty the fire in the furnace. And we'll get going. It's late."

"But we can't. We haven't started to eat yet."

"Why not? It's practically eight o'clock. Don't you want to go to the Rotarys?"

"Sure. Who'd want to miss seeing the executive secretary get sawed in half? Of course, I want to go."

"Of course he does!" My mother stopped waving her apron.

"All we got left to do is eat. It won't take more than a couple of minutes."

"Besides there's the others," my mother told my father. "Herm Ries and Mr. Hemmendinger, they're waiting for their boys too."

"There's a half hour," my father looked at his watch. "That ought to give you enough time. Get going, Andy. I'll wait for you."

"And don't gulp," said my mother. "There's plenty of time to eat properly."

We had the cellar to air out, and the stuff to put away that we stuck up, and the fire to dump into the furnace before we started eating. And when we did sit down at the table, John took out of his overcoat some big thick plumbers' candles, the kind that sell at six for a quarter. Everyone had a lighted candle in front of his plate. As far as making the place hard to recognize the candles turned out better than the decorations. They changed even us. We looked more serious, each of us sitting in the dark behind a little flame.

At last, we started. Bo poured out the ginger ale. Then John stood up and held his glass and rattled away for a couple of minutes.

"He hopes we won't get distemper," I told the others. "And we get through the winter. It's a toast. Everyone has to give a toast."

Bitsy thought a bit and got up. "Melba," he said. "That's a toast." Eech got up and said, "French." I said, "Dry." And Bo said, "Buttered." We drank our ginger ale.

No one got drunk. We went to work on our rice pudding, talking about broomsticks, the kind witches ride.

By then we'd worked our way past Napoleons, cream puffs and eclairs and reached our main course, the Mocha Cake with the writing on it. John stopped to get his fiddle out of the burlap bag when Bo looked at the wrist watch he wears. "Holy Hannah. It's eight-thirty. My old man's waiting to go to the Rotarys."

"Mine too," said Each.

"We'd better get out of here," said Bits.

"Without any cake?" Each put down the eclair he was eating.

"Maybe we can get a couple of more minutes, if it's okay to be a little late." I stood up from the table. "I'll be right back."

The kitchen was dark when I got upstairs. My mother was in the living room having coffee with Eechee's Ma and Mrs. Hemmendinger and Mrs. Kinnoy.

"Your father's at the club," she told me before I had a chance to ask. "He went on ahead with Herman and Mr. Hemmendinger. They're waiting for you there."

"If it's only a couple of more minutes, do you think they'd mind?"

"Pa asked me to give you a message. He says he's leaving this up to your judgment. You can come over whenever you're finished."

"Whenever?" That sounded like a good arrangement.

"Your father says you're welcome any time at all."

"Any time at all," I told the others when I got downstairs. They were relieved to hear there wasn't any rush. Especially when Onion John got started with his fiddle.

He was down at the end of the cellar where it was black except for a square red glow, like a stage, lighted up by the open furnace door. The violin John had was a wreck, patched all over with friction tape. But the sounds that came out were as good as new.

The number John played reminded you a little of "Old Mc-Donald Had a Farm" except it was lowered a couple of notches and came out ten times slower.

Onion John had a couple of faster numbers, with more snap to them. There was a dance went with the last one. It was called a Clock Dance and John did it by going around in a circle, stomping heels and scissoring his feet on the curves. He did it twice around, playing the fiddle all the while. None of us could ever do it without tripping.

By then we'd finished eating and the Mocha Cake that was left over spelled out a word. There was 'Hem' for Hemmendinger. 'Arz' from Schwarz. 'Ri' from Ries. and 'Ch' from Rusch. Hemarzrich. It sounded like Onion John's kind of word. But it didn't mean anything in his language either. We decided we'd make it a secret word. To mean *trouble*. We arranged when anyone of us was in trouble, all he'd have to say was *Hemarzrich,* and the others would have to help.

In my judgment, it was time we got over to the Rotarys. The candles were burning out, anyway, and the brightest part of the cellar was in front where the moonlight came in through the window.

It was when Onion John saw the moon that the big delay came. It was a perfect moon for making gold, full and near in a wide clean sky. But the miracle was, it came on Halloween! Never in Onion John's life had the two come together on the same night before. It meant, with his eyes wide John whispered, our fortunes were made.

What decided us we had the time to make our fortunes was the sight of Mr. Kinnoy, the executive secretary, walking down the empty street.

"He's whole," said Bitz. "They must've called off the program."

We went ahead with Onion John. He had everything he needed for stewing gold in his burlap bag, fern seeds and some sticks of lead, wood alcohol and some special stones, the kind that philosophers used. By rights, we had to be in clean clothes but I found some sheets on the back line to wrap ourselves in. What with prayers and washing up and hymns and a little meditating again, there was a lot of preparation before we had a pot filled with the proper ingredients.

John put it into the furnace. He poured wood alcohol in the pot and a blue flame came out. He began a deep hum and he started to sway. Standing there in front of the furnace door, watching the flame, the four of us picked up his sway.

I heard a whisper. "Andy." It was my mother, far off. I listened and it came again, "Andy."

I swayed backwards a couple of steps and sneaked off without bothering the others. Before I got through the dark to the top of the kitchen stairs, my mother said, "It's after one."

When I came into sight she asked, "Is that my sheet?" She didn't wait for an answer. "This is no time to be playing ghosts!"

"We're not." I came into the kitchen and when I could see again, there was my father standing. "We're making gold."

My father interrupted my mother. "Okay, Andy. Ask him to leave."

"Who? Onion John? We wouldn't know how to go on without him."

"Get that man out of this house!"

"He's run into a miracle. It's the first time it ever happened in all his life."

"I don't care about that, Andy."

"Can't you humor him, just a bit more?"

"Not any more."

By now my eyes were accustomed to the kitchen and I looked around at everything. The refrigerator broke out with a high hum.

"You just want me to get him out of here?"

"That's all."

"It's my fault we didn't get over to the Rotarys. We went by my judgment."

That didn't make any difference to my father and mother. They stood there looking at me in the sheet. I took it off and I folded it carefully.

"If you'd tell me what you want me to do," I asked my mother, "with the sheet?"

She took it out of my hands.

I went back down into the dark again. "Hemarzrich," I said to the others at the furnace. I never thought I'd get to use the word so soon.

It worked, for a secret word, the way we'd arranged. They put on the light. I told Onion John what he had to do. I figured he'd cry because he never cares who's around. Instead, he rubbed his mustache into shape.

They gave me their sheets, until I had an armful. Onion John picked up his burlap bag and the four of them left. I didn't know where to put the sheets down, not in the dirty cellar. I was lucky to find a laundry basket near the door. I took out the pot that was stewing in the furnace and I dumped it into the ash barrel. Everything, except for Onion John's stones. I picked those out so I could give them back to Onion John next time I saw him, whenever that'd be.

—JOSEPH KRUMGOLD

From Ghoulies and Ghosties

In many lands various charms, amulets, and rituals have been used to save people when they become frightened by what seems spooky and strange. Often people have joined together in prayers and chants for protection. Here from the British Isles is a very old chant that is well-known today.

From Ghoulies and Ghosties,
Long-leggety Beasties,
And Things that go bump in the night,
Good Lord, preserve us.

Index

219

Designer—David S. Wilson
Typeface—14 point Granjon
Typesetter—Parthenon Press
Manufacturer—Parthenon Press